YOUTH AND THE DRUG PROBLEM

A Guide for Parents and Teachers

YOUTH AND THE DRUG PROBLEM

A Guide for Parents and Teachers

By

HAROLD D. LOVE, Ed. D.

State College of Arkansas
Conway, Arkansas

With a Foreword by

William H. Osborne

Drug Education Program
State of Arkansas

CHARLES C THOMAS • PUBLISHER
Springfield • Illinois • U.S.A.

613.8
L 897

Published and Distributed Throughout the World by
CHARLES C THOMAS • PUBLISHER
BANNERSTONE HOUSE
301-327 East Lawrence Avenue, Springfield, Illinois, U.S.A.
NATCHEZ PLANTATION HOUSE
735 North Atlantic Boulevard, Fort Lauderdale, Florida, U.S.A.

© *1971, by* CHARLES C THOMAS • PUBLISHER

Library of Congress Catalog Card Number: 79-143748

With THOMAS BOOKS *careful attention is given to all details of*
manufacturing and design. It is the Publisher's desire to present books
that are satisfactory as to their physical qualities and artistic possibilities
and appropriate for their particular use. THOMAS BOOKS will be true
to those laws of quality that assure a good name and good will.

Printed in the United States of America
0-5

To Sharon
who knows much about the
devastating effects of drug abuse
on the adjustment of an entire family,
. . . this book is dedicated.

FOREWORD

Historically, we have been content to delegate to law enforcement officials full responsibility for control of the illegal use of drugs. "Pushers" were despicable and "users" were just as guilty, and we could be content with our self-righteousness because drug abuse was mostly a problem of the very poor. How were we to know that approximately every forty years the drug problem becomes particularly acute and spills from the ghetto into other sections of society?

But times have changed. News media, radio, newspapers, and television are emphasizing that drug abuse extends through all levels of society and all persons are potential prey to its influence. We are becoming aware that young people are rejecting the primary drug of older people—alcohol—and are turning to other means for escape. As time passes we are also realizing that enforcement procedures are ineffective means of controlling drug abuse and that our best alternative is to educate parents, teachers, and young people.

Prevention of illegal use of drugs by young people will require alterations in many programs and in many people.

The educational system must offer young people the opportunity to see for themselves that drug abuse contains more dangers than it does pleasures and that more viable options for being "turned on" exist. At the same time, though, the system must provide the basis for these options. That is, the school must offer programs relevant to learning and behavioral needs in order for students to rediscover that learning is an exhilarating experience.

The adult world must offer clearly defined pathways so that young people can see themselves as important in society's scheme of things. And we adults must increase our credibility as models. Our actions, not our words, govern the way young people perceive us.

I am delighted this book has been written. I hope educators and parents pay attention to it. It has long been said that education is the best answer to our problems, and it is time we put this saying to the test.

WILLIAM H. OSBORNE

PREFACE

Drug abuse and drug dependence among our children and youth are threatening to become commonplace. In the past, drug abusers have been identified as products of the lower classes—the ghetto and poverty; yet drug dependence is spreading with appalling speed into the middle and upper classes and into younger and younger age groups.

Inadequate understanding and identification of drugs are among the major difficulties in dealing with the problem. Many times it is parents who know the least about drugs; yet, ironically, it is they who need to be best informed. Many parents are startled by the amount of knowledge and seeming sophistication their children have on the subject, while others find themselves helplessly unable to answer the questions which their children ask them about drugs. So this book is for parents, to help them face this serious problem of drug abuse directly and intellingently.

But parents cannot carry this burden alone. Physicians, educators, ministers, and counselors must be prepared to help. This book is for them also.

This book deals with the definition and explanation of drug abuse, a brief history of drug dependence, and the motivational patterns in drug usage.

Concerned persons have the grim responsibility of watching for signs of drug dependence in children and youth. Hopefully, this treatise will be beneficial to them in this realm. In this publication the recognition of drug abusers is discussed along with information concerning each drug: the pharmaceutical name, brand names, slang names, medical classification, medical uses, a description of the drug's primary and secondary effects, a description of the drug's physical properties and appearance, the different ways drugs may be taken, and the penalty for illegal possession.

Parents and others should know where to go for help if or when they find evidence of drug abuse. This book deals with the treatment for drug abusers as well as legal controls and prevention of drug abuse. Prevention is certainly the most effective treatment, and positive action *is* possible both in public policy and in the behavior of individuals.

This book has developed out of a deep and growing concern for the grave problem of drug abuse among our young. It is hoped that all who read it will be enlightened and better prepared to meet this monumental problem which is endangering our children's lives.

The development of this publication was not only guided by the author, but a physician and minister, both interested and knowledgable in the use of drugs, read the chapters and made professional suggestions.

I should like to thank my family physician, Dr. Robert B. Benafield, who read and criticized the manuscript from a physician's viewpoint. I should also like to thank his wife, Helen Benafield, who read and criticized the manuscript from a parent's viewpoint. Many students from my research class contributed invaluable information to this publication. I should also like to thank the drug abusers who volunteered information and the many people who were interviewed.

I should like to thank Mrs. Jon Guthrie who helped in several areas of the manuscript's preparation and W. H. Osborne from Governor Rockefeller's office for writing the introduction. Katty Crownover should be singled out for not only typing the manuscript but proofreading it as well. Lastly, I should like to thank my wife, Sue, not only for reading the manuscript but for proofreading and encouraging the preparation in all phases of this work.

H. D. L.

CONTENTS

YOUTH AND THE DRUG PROBLEM

A Guide for Parents and Teachers

SECTION I

Chapter I

DEFINING THE DRUG PROBLEM

D rug abuse is many things. It is the heroin user injecting his bag of "H," the Methedrine® user high on "speed," the college student smoking "pot," and the junior high school student sniffing model airplane glue. But it is also the adult with a persistent headache or toothache taking more and more "pain pills," or the adult starting his day with a "pep pill" for a needed "pick-me-up" and ending it with several drinks to "unwind" and a sleeping pill to put him to sleep. It is interesting to note that it is adults, not young people, who are the main consumers of tranquilizers, pep pills, addictive sleeping pills, brain-damaging drugs like alcohol, and cancer-producing agents like cigarettes.

Drug abuse is a complex problem. It is a problem which the very mention of arouses much anxiety, fear, anger, and irrationality. One of the rudimentary problems of drug abuse is the confusion of terminology. Basic to the understanding of the problem is an accurate knowledge of the related terms—physical dependence, tolerance, psychological dependence, addiction, habituation, and drug dependence. With repeated use, many drugs cause *physical dependence*. There is a state whereby the body requires continued administration of the drug in order to function. Body functioning is interfered with if the drug is withdrawn, and withdrawal symptoms appear in a pattern specific for the drug. The total reaction to deprivation is known clinically as an *abstinence syndrome*. The symptoms that appear depend on the amount and kind of drug used. The withdrawal symptoms are usually the only dependable evidence as to whether or not physical dependence has developed, and their insensitiveness is taken as an index of the severity of the physical dependence. Withdrawal symptoms disappear as the body once again adjusts to being without the drug—or if the drug is reintroduced.

With many drugs, the chronic user finds he must constantly increase the dose in order to produce the same effects as that from the initial dose. This phenomenon, called *tolerance,* represents the body's ability to adapt to the presence of a foreign substance. Tolerance does not develop for all drugs or in all individuals; but with drugs such as morphine, addicts have been known to build up great tolerance very quickly. It is interesting to note, however, that tolerance does not develop for all the possible effects of a given drug. For example, tolerance develops to the euphoric-like effects of heroin, but only slightly to constricting effects on the pupil of the eye. *Complete tolerance* may not develop to a drug's toxic effects; accordingly, no matter how high his tolerance, an addict may still administer a lethal dose to himself. *Cross-tolerance* refers to the fact that tolerance development for one drug may also result in tolerance for similar drugs.

A more important factor in keeping the abuser enslaved by his habit is the *psychic* or *psychological dependence* present in most cases of drug abuse. Psychic analogy is the fact that an individual does not physically need to drink tea or coffee or to watch television, but the person can become so used to the habit that he feels he cannot live without it. Thus in psychological dependence on a drug, the abuser not only likes the feeling from the drug and wants to reexperience it—he feels a definite need for the expected drug effects, a need which may be mild or intense or even compulsive. The drug enables him to escape from reality—from his problems, anxieties, and frustrations. With the drug, all seems well. It is the psychological factor which causes an addict who has been withdrawn from his physical dependence to return to drug abuse. Psychic dependence on a drug may develop independently of whether or not the drug has produced either physical dependence or tolerance or both.

Three frequently confused terms encountered in drug abuse discussions are *addiction, habituation,* and *drug dependence.* Addiction is the state of periodic or chronic intoxication produced by the repeated consumption of a drug and involves tolerance, psychological dependence, usually physical dependence, and an overwhelming compulsion to continue using the drug. Thus the drug experimenter is frequently erroneously labeled an "addict." Detrimental effects of addiction are on both the individual and society. Habituation is defined as a condition, resulting from the repeated consumption of a drug, which involves little or no evidence of tolerance, some psychological dependence, no physical dependence, and a desire (but not a compulsion) to continue taking the drug for the feeling of well-being that it engenders. Detrimental effects, if any, are primarily on the individual. Through the years, the terms addiction and habituation have frequently been used interchangeably—and obviously erroneously so. The World Health Organization recently recommended that these terms be replaced by a single and more general term—*drug dependence.*

Drug dependence is described as a state arising from repeated administration of a drug on a periodic and continuous basis. Since many different kinds of drugs can be involved in drug dependence, the term is further qualified in accordance with the particular drug being used, for example, drug dependence of the morphine type or drug dependence of the barbiturate type. It was the hope of the World Health Organization that the new term drug dependence would replace the older terms of *addiction* and *habituation,* but from a practical standpoint this is not possible. The language of laws, international, national, and local, which governs drugs subject to abuse, encompasses the terms addiction and habituation. Thus it appears that all three terms will become a part of drug abuse terminology, with the term drug dependence being favored by medically oriented groups and the terms addiction and habituation being favored in legislative and law enforcement circles.

How many persons use drugs? The answer depends entirely on how we define drug use and drug abuse. Most surveys count as a user any individual who has ever touched marijuana or any other hallucinogenic drug, and some surveys also include persons who occasionally have taken amphetamines or barbiturates. To label such individuals as drug abusers is like applying the term smoker to the individual who once, at the age of twelve, smoked part of a cigarette behind the barn but was sick and decided he would never smoke again. Probably the largest single group sometimes labeled as drug abusers consists of those individuals who once or twice tried marijuana but have no plans to continue.

Dr. Kenneth Keniston, a Yale University psychologist who has closely studied the subject of drug abuse, suggests drug users can be divided into three types—the "tasters," the "seekers," and the "heads." Tasters are the individuals who have tried one or more drugs, usually marijuana and possibly LSD, and have no plans to continue. They constitute the largest group of the users. The seekers are the persons who use drugs occasionally, as on weekends and in social gatherings and who plan to continue their experimentation. Drugs for them are for "kicks" or just the experience. Although these people take occasional trips with marijuana, LSD, or peyote, they have not organized their lives around drugs. The heads constitute a considerably smaller group. These are the "hard-core" addicts, those for whom drug use and the drug group have become, at least temporarily, an exclusive or dominating concern and activity. Their activities revolve almost entirely around drug experiences and securing supplies. They have been on drugs for some time and presently feel that they cannot function without drug support. Obviously there is much overlapping between the latter two groups, and a seeker may deteriorate to the heads group. The transition occurs when the interaction between drug effects and personality causes a loss of control over drug use. The drug becomes a means of solving or avoiding life's problems.

The problem of drugs is a problem of ignorance—lack of knowledge about the effects of most drugs on the human mind. And this is as true of aspirin as it is of LSD (lysergic acid diethylamide). The action of most drugs is extremely complex and involves many processes, many of which we now know very little about. The drug effects are not predictable as they depend on the individual's personality, his state of mind, the dosage, the situation, his expectations, and even the company he keeps. Consequently, as a result of this lack of knowledge, there has been too much propaganda about drugs, both for and against.

It is a problem of a "pill society." Americans seem to accept the well-advertised proposition that there is a chemical solution for any problem of unpleasantness and discomfort, whether it be physical, psychological, or social. We are familiar with such slogans as: "Headache, take aspirin; tension, take the little blue pill." "Happiness is just a swallow away." "Take a pill and sleep like a baby." "If you're depressed take capsule A." "To lose weight take the X tablet."

Finally, the drug problem is a symptom of far deeper, more complex human problems. The real problem is not drugs but the people who use drugs. It is increasingly evident that people with problems—personal, social, and intellectual—use drugs, and it is the individual with his reason for using drugs that is the key to understanding abuse. Adults with their alcohol and tranquilizers and students with their marijuana and LSD are both reacting to conditions which negate human values and human worth.

Addiction to hard drugs is a chronic form of suicide—a form of self-destruction. Very often the potential addict sees all too clearly the mess around him in his own life, the violence and destruction in society, which shows itself in everyday living, and consciously or unconsciously, chooses self-destruction rather than take part in the society around him whose values disgust him. Thus to eliminate drug problems we need to look beyond them to the kind of persons we want to be and to the kind of society in which we believe.

Chapter II

THE ABUSABLE DRUGS

T he list of abusable drugs can conveniently be divided into five categories: sedatives, stimulants, hallucinogens, narcotics, and organic solvents.

SEDATIVES

The sedatives include a variety of old and new drugs manufactured for medical purposes to relax the central nervous system. They are prescribed to induce sleep, or in smaller doses, to provide a calming effect. Sleeping pills, muscle relaxants, tranquilizers, and many antihistimines fall into this category.

✓ Barbiturates

By far the best known and most frequently abused of the sedatives are the barbiturates. Barbiturates are generally classified in terms of duration of action. The short to intermediate acting barbiturates are the ones most commonly abused, and include pentobarbital sodium (Nembutal®) and secobarbital sodium (Seconal®). Commonly used slang terms for these pills include *barbs, goof balls*, and *downers*. Barbiturates are usually taken orally as a tablet or capsule, although they can be taken intravenously.

The versatility of barbiturates is evidenced by their use in the treatment of epilepsy, high blood pressure, and insomnia. They are also used in the treatment and diagnosis of mental disorders as well as to relax patients before and during surgery. Barbiturates are generally depressants. Taken in medically supervised doses, they mildly depress actions of the nerves, skeletal muscles, and the heart muscles. They slow down heart rate and breathing and lower blood pressure. Small amounts make the user relaxed, sociable, and good humored. In higher doses the effects resemble alcohol intoxication. The speech of the user is thick. He staggers and may become sluggish, gloomy, and sometimes irritable and quarrelsome. The ability to think, concentrate, and work is impaired; emotional control is weakened. The abuser may finally fall into deep sleep. Death from over-dosage results from depressed respiratory function.

Self-medication with alcohol and "over-the-counter" prescription sedatives are common in today's society where anxiety, stress, and insomnia are prevalent. Unfortunately, social accept-ance of this kind of self-medication seems to be increasing. However, barbiturates are extremely dangerous when taken without medical advice and prescription. Because doctors com-monly prescribe these drugs, many people mistakenly consider them safe to use freely and as they choose. *They are not.* Bar-biturates are high on the list of suicidal poisons. These suicides may be either intentional or unintentional. If accurate figures were available, the number of nationally known persons dying directly from barbiturate abuse is not infrequent. The user may erroneously perceive the passage of time between doses or may become confused about how many pills he has taken and die of an accidental overdose. Also, sometimes for various reasons, the absorption rate of the drugs may be slowed. The user, not getting the desired effect within what seems to him a long time, continues to take tablet after tablet until he is unconscious. In the process, he may ingest a lethal dose.

Barbiturates are particularly dangerous when combined with other drugs. The cumulative effects can easily result in very serious intoxication or death. The combination of barbiturates and alcohol are an important cause of automobile accidents, as barbiturates tend to heighten the effects of alcohol. The tragic suicide cases, due to an overdose of barbiturates combined with alcohol, of several movie stars are well known.

Essentially, there are four types of barbiturate drug abuse, and they overlap only occasionally. In the first type are persons seeking the sedative effects of the drug in order to deal with states of emotional distress. This pattern may be carried to such a degree that the person looks for almost total oblivion and semi-permanent stupor. In the second type there are users for whom the drugs now stimulate rather than depress due to prolonged use. Thus barbiturates are taken to exhilarate and animate the user to so-called increased efficiency. In the third type are persons who take barbiturates to counteract abuse effects of various stimulant drugs such as amphetamines. A familiar example is the individual who takes pep pills to function in the daytime, and then takes a sedative to sleep at night. In the fourth category, barbiturate abuse is found in combination with other types of drug abuse, mainly alcohol and/or opiates. Many authorities attempt to counteract the withdrawal effects of alcohol with barbiturates. Frequently, alcohol and barbiturates are combined in an attempt to obtain effects that surpass those of either.

Barbiturates are physically addicting. Severe physical dependence on barbiturates is very dangerous and is far more serious than physical dependence on opium, morphine, and heroin. Many experts consider barbiturate addiction more difficult to cure than narcotic dependence. The body needs increasingly high doses to feel the effects, and when the drugs are withdrawn abruptly, the abuser suffers from cramps, nausea, delirium, convulsions, stupor, coma, and in some cases death. Therefore, withdrawal should take place in a hospital over a period of several weeks on gradual reduced dosages. It takes several months for the body to return to normal after long-term barbiturate abuse.

Nonbarbiturate Sedatives

A number of nonbarbiturate sedatives used medically to induce sleep and for sedation are also capable of being abused. With chronic use of high doses, tolerance, physical dependence, and psychological dependence can develop. Because of their abuse potential, several of these drugs have become subject to the regulations of the Drug Abuse Control Amendments of 1965. Glutethimide, ethchlorvynol, ethinamate, and methyprylon are examples of the newer sedatives which are now controlled.

Tranquilizers

Tranquilizers are another group of drugs which occasionally have been abused. Unlike barbiturate-type sedatives, tranquilizers can be used to counteract tension and anxiety without producing sleep or significantly impairing mental and physical function. The two tranquilizers most often reported abused are meprobamate and chlordiazepoxide. Chronic abuse of these drugs, involving increasingly larger daily doses, may result in the development of physical and/or psychological dependence. Symptoms during misuse and following abrupt withdrawal closely resemble those seen with barbiturates. To date, abuse of tranquilizers has been infrequent and has not become a "street" problem.

STIMULANTS

This group includes drugs which directly stimulate the central nervous system. The most widely known stimulant in this country is caffeine, an ingredient of coffee, tea, cola, and other beverages. Since the effects of caffein are relatively mild, its usage is socially acceptable and not an abuse problem. The synthetic stimulants such as amphetamine and other closely related drugs are more potent and can be abused. Another dangerous stimulant is cocaine; however, cocaine will be dealt with later, as it is classified legally but not chemically as a narcotic drug.

Stimulants are prescribed in medical practice to reduce appetite, to treat mild depression, and to control the symptoms of narcolepsy (a disease characterized by involuntary attacks of sleep). These drugs are used to induce insomnia and counteract fatigue in persons occasionally required to perform mental or physical tasks of long duration (as evidenced in the use of amphetamines by the astronauts) and to counteract excessive drowsiness caused by sedative drugs. Paradoxically, stimulants tend to calm hyperactive, noisy, aggressive children, thus producing more normal behavior.

Amphetamines

Amphetamines are the most widely abused stimulants. Benezedrine®, Dexedrine®, and Methedrine are the most commonly used. Benezedrine and Dexedrine have historically been popular with truck drivers for keeping awake on long hauls that require more abundant energy sources than the body naturally possesses. Methedrine (speed) has become enormously popular among the drug users seeking a new high. It is the alternative which has been chosen by large numbers of those who turned from LSD following evidence that the latter could produce long-term mental and genetic deficiencies.

When properly prescribed by a physician, moderate doses of amphetamine can check fatigue and produce feelings of alertness, self-confidence, and well-being. These factors explain the amphetamines' popular name—pep pills. In some people these feelings are followed by a letdown feeling or depression hangover. Heavier doses cause an increase in psychological tension manifested by jitteryness, irritability, and unclear speech. People on very large doses of amphetamines appear withdrawn, with their emotions dulled, and then seem unable to organize their thinking.

Amphetamines may increase heart rate, cause palpitations (throbbing heart and rapid breathing), dilate the pupils, and cause dry mouth, sweating, headache, diarrhea, and pallor. Typically the blood pressure rises, but it may fluctuate or even fall. The effects of amphetamines on the digestive system are unpredictable; if intestinal activity is pronounced it may reduce it, but if already reduced, it may increase it. Such effects are generally seen only with high doses or as occasional side effects with therapeutic doses. Amphetamines seldom cause death, even in acute overdosage.

The stimulant drugs are usually taken orally, but there are reports of an increasing tendency among those who use amphetamines for "kicks" to take the drug, primarily Methedrine, by intravenous injection, since the more rapid absorption results in a more potent effect. This is a dangerous practice known among abusers as *speeding*. Most persons are familiar with the slogan "Speed Kills" which refers to this dramatic pattern of abuse.

All kinds of people misuse amphetamines—from the middle-aged businessman or housewife, to students, athletes, and truck drivers. Recent government surveys show that young people are becoming the greatest abusers of these drugs. Drivers take them to stay awake on long trips, students take them while cramming for exams, and athletes take them, although sporting associations have banned their use. Some persons try them for a temporary kick. Some abusers reach a point where they need both stimulant and sedative drugs to get a chemical "up" and a chemical "down."

The stimulant drugs do not produce physical dependence. Although the body does not become physically dependent on their continued use, it does develop a tolerance to these drugs so that larger and larger doses are required to feel the effects. However, stimulants are psychologically addicting, meaning that a practice can become a habit for mental or emotional reasons, with the person getting used to turning to the drug for its effects.

Stimulant drugs are dangerous in that these drugs can drive a person to do things beyond his physical endurance that leave him exhausted, or they can mask underlying fatigue and make it impossible to accurately judge one's performance. Many automobile, industrial, and recreational accidents are related to reckless behavior due to the influence of amphetamines. Pep pills are not a magic source of extra mental or physical energy; they serve only to push the user to a greater expenditure of his own resources, sometimes to a hazardous point that is often not recognized. Heavy doses may cause a temporary paranoid psychosis (mental illness) which requires hospitalization. This is usually accompanied by auditory and/or visual hallucinations. Abruptly withdrawing the drug from the heavy abuser can result in a deep, suicidal depression.

Long-term heavy users of the amphetamines are usually irritable and unstable and, like other heavy drug abusers, they show varying degrees of social, intellectual, economic, and emotional deterioration.

Dangers from injecting *speed* into the vein include serum hepatitis, abscesses, and even death in the case of unaccustomed high doses. Injection of "speed" causes abnormal heart rates and may result in serious psychotic states and long-term personality disorders.

There are a number of other stimulant drugs which, while not closely related to amphetamine chemically, do have similar uses and effects. Such a drug is phenmetrazine, used medically in the treatment of obesity. Phenmetrazine has been placed under the same controls imposed upon amphetamine. These miscellaneous stimulants are not as widely misused as amphetamine drugs, although when abused, they can produce all of the effects associated with the abuse of amphetamine.

HALLUCINOGENS

Distortions of perception, dream images, and hallucinations are characteristic of the group of drugs called hallucinogens or mind-affecting drugs. In practice these drugs actually produce more distortion (seeing or hearing things in a different way than they actually are) than hallucinations (seeing or hearing things not present). Hallucinogens are unique among drugs that cause dependence in that they actually are not accepted for use in medical practice. They are not manufactured for professional or medical reasons, but are made under scientific conditions by amateurs. They are usually highly impure and dangerously unreliable from a dosage standpoint.

Marijuana

Marijuana is first in popularity of this group, but last in terms of potency. LSD, DMT(dimethyltryptamine), STP, and Mescaline (peyote) are less well-known psychedelic agents.

Marijuana is one of the least understood of all naturally occurring drugs, although it has been known for nearly five thousand years. Most widely used in Asia and Africa, it was introduced in this country in 1920. In 1937 the Federal Marijuana Act outlawed its general use.

It is important to recognize that marijuana is a term used to refer to particular forms of cannabis which are widespead in North America. Cannabis is obtained from the common hemp plant which grows wild in most temperate climates in the world. The fibers of its stalks are widely used for the manufacture of rope. The substance cannabis is derived from a resin exuded by the female plant. The leaves, stems, and flowering tops may be dried and crushed or chopped into small pieces to produce the marijuana common in Mexico and in the United States. Frequently, the term marijuana is used indiscriminately to refer to cannabis of all kinds and potencies. Much of the controversy about the effects of marijuana is a result of this confusion. In this country some of the vigorous opponents of marijuana seem to foster this confusion by attributing to any use of marijuana the effects produced primarily by excessive use of the more potent forms of cannabis.

At one time, marijuana had a minor place in the practice of medicine. But because the safety and effectiveness of newer drugs so outweigh the limited utility of marijuana, it is no longer considered medically respectable in the United States.

Marijuana may be smoked, sniffed, or ingested, but effects are experienced most quickly with smoking. While occasionally smoked in pipes, marijuana is smoked most often in the form of cigarettes known as *reefers, sticks,* and *weeds.* Common nicknames in this country for marijuana are *pot, tea, grass, weed,* and *Mary Jane.* The smoke from marijuana is harsh and smells like burnt rope or dried grass. Its sweeter odor is easily recognized.

When smoked, marijuana quickly enters the bloodstream and acts upon the brain. Because it affects mood and thinking and may cause hallucinations, it is classified as a mild hallucinogen. The effects of marijuana, even more than those of many other drugs, are variable in different individuals and in the same individual at different times. The effects depend on the personality of the user, the dose, the route of administration, and the specific circumstances in which the drug is used. The effects are also a function of learning to smoke properly, of being tutored recognizing and labeling effects, and of becoming sensitized to the effects. In most individuals, these effects are pleasurable at low dosage levels and unpleasant at higher dosage levels. Common effects have been variously described as a feeling of contentment and inner satisfaction; free play of the imagination; exhilaration of spirit; the feeling of floating above reality; ideas disconnected, uncontrollable, and freeflowing; minutes seeming like hours; space broadened; near objects seeming distant; uncontrollable laughter and hilarity. This may be followed by moody reverie, with or without depression. In some individuals and under some circumstances the depression may be the initial response and be followed by the "high." At higher dosage levels, extremely vivid hallucinations may occur, with the content highly dependent on the personality of the individual.

In terms of some effects on behavior, use of marijuana is roughly comparable to moderate abuse of alcohol. Like alcohol, it tends to loosen inhibitions and increase suggestibility, which explains why an individual under the influence of marijuana may engage in activities he would not ordinarily consider. One of the dangers of marijuana is that the drug can have unpredictable effects—even on persons accustomed to its use.

Marijuana does not produce physical dependence or withdrawal symptoms. Once the user has established the amount of marijuana needed to achieve his particular "high," there is little tendency to increase the dose, indicating that tolerance does not develop. Moderate to strong psychic dependence can develop in accordance with the user's appreciation of the drug's effects.

Marijuana has been blamed as a cause for criminal behavior, addiction to heroin, psychoses, mental deterioration, and traffic accidents. Careful investigation does not substantiate any of these causal claims. There is no reliable evidence that marijuana causes crime other than that involved in acquiring or possessing the drug, although certainly criminals may use marijuana. Data with respect to traffic accidents is lacking although many experienced users of marijuana concede that a person who is "high" or "stoned" should not drive.

The National Institute of Health recently released a report stating that there is no reliable evidence that marijuana smoking necessarily leads to heroin addiction. While it is estimated that less than 5 percent of marijuana users will try heroin or other hard drugs, 85 percent of all heroin addicts admit prior marijuana smoking. Generally, people who become seriously involved with one drug often become involved with many drugs. It is not known if marijuana use causes any organic brain damage or has any toxic effect on the body. Yet "no reliable evidence" or "a lack of knowledge" cannot be the final answer. The health lesson gained from recent studies on the long-term use of tobacco exemplifies why caution must be taken before pronouncing marijuana physically harmless. Good controlled research, both laboratory and field studies, is desperately needed. In order to produce dependable data, such studies must be designed with proper consideration of the many complex factors which contribute to drug effects and to repeated use of a drug. These include the purity and amount of the drug, the physiological and psychological state of the user, his beliefs, personality characteristics and life history, the setting, and the relevant characteristics of the experimenter or supplier.

For certain, marijuana is known to be an intoxicant and like any intoxicant can affect mental judgment and physical coordination.

LSD

Lysergic acid diethylamide, a man-made chemical, is the most potent of the hallucinogens. It is so powerful that a single ounce will produce 300,000 human doses. An amount literally smaller than a grain of salt can produce gross psychotic reactions in human beings.

On the illicit market, the drug may be obtained as a small white pill, as a crystalline powder in capsules, or as a tasteless, colorless, or odorless liquid in ampuls. Frequently, it is offered in the form of saturated sugar cubes, cookies, or crackers. LSD is usually taken orally, but may be injected.

An average dose of LSD has an effect that usually lasts from eight to ten hours. Besides producing hallucinations, the drug will cause a rise in blood pressure and temperature, dilate the pupils, produce tremors of the hands, cold sweat, nausea, vomiting, and a loss of appetite. Just how LSD works in the body is not yet known, but is seems to affect the levels of certain chemicals in the brain and to produce changes in the brain's electrical activity. LSD is not physically addicting.

Users of LSD say it has a wide variety of effects. Basically, the user's perception of himself in time and space is distorted. Taste, smell, hearing, touch, and vision inaccurately seem more acute. Flat objects take on three dimensional shapes. Walls may appear to move; colors seem stronger and more brilliant. One sensory impression may be translated or merged into another; for example, music may appear as color, colors may seem to have taste. One of the most confusing yet common reactions among users is the feeling of two strong and opposite emotions at the same time—they can feel both happy and sad at once or relaxed and tense. Among the other effects of LSD on the user is the loss of his sense of time. He does not know how much time is passing, but he does remain conscious.

Whether a trip is "good" or "bad" depends on a combination of factors, including the user's motives and attitudes, the nature of his companionship at the time of the trip, the physical surroundings, and possibly the purity of the drug itself. During a "good trip" the individual may have the *illusion* that he is gaining great insights into his personality and behavior. This is because notions that come to the user in the highly suggestible drugged state seem much more "real." It is doubtful, however, that valid insights occur with any regularity. On a "bad trip" almost anything can happen. The sense of losing control during hallucinations can cause the individual to panic. Hospitalization may be sought by the user or a companion, neither of whom can cope with the sense of terror. Horrible delusions that seem terrifyingly real can cause personality-shattering psychotic breaks with reality which may last days or years after the drug has worn off. Because of feelings of omniscience and indestructibility, the "tripper" may believe he can fly—and plunge to his death from a high window as some have done. Or he may drive or walk in front of a moving car because he thinks he cannot be harmed.

In addition to the danger of the unpredictability of the effects of LSD on the individual, another critical aspect is that a user

can "trip" on LSD without having taken the drug at that time.
The LSD experience can recur spontaneously weeks or months
after a user last took the drug. Such "flashbacks" are most
common during physical or psychological stress but can also
be brought on unexpectedly by some common medicines.

LSD and its closely related compounds, DMT and STP, are
probably the most dangerous drugs frequently experimented
with by young people. Suicides, accidental deaths, panic reactions,
depressive reactions, and permanent severe mental derangement
can result from single or repeated experiences with the drugs.
In addition, there is a distinct possibility of chromosomal aber-
rations and future birth abnormalities following usage. Until
further research throws more light on the question, medical
authorities warn that the drug may be considered a definite risk,
and women of child-bearing age are particularly advised not to
use the drug.

Mescaline

Mescaline, which comes from the cactus plant, is another
of the well-known drugs associated with mind-distorting properties. It is available on the illicit market as a crystalline powder
in capsules or as a liquid in ampuls or vials. It may also be
obtained as whole cactus "buttons," chopped buttons in capsules,
or as a brownish-gray cloudy liquid. "Mesc" or "big chief" is
generally taken orally, but may be injected. Because of its
bitter taste, mescaline is often taken along with some other
substance such as hot cocoa or orange juice. Even though the
use of mescaline is now in the experimental stage, it is believed
this drug provides powerful effects almost identical to LSD.
The effects may last as long as ten hours or more.

Peyote

Like mescaline, peyote is obtained from the cactus plant.
Peyote buttons are usually chopped and brewed with tea or
chewed while drinking wine or some other highly flavored
drink in order to mask its bad taste. Peyote is also known as
"moon" and "p."

Psilocybin

Psilocybin is derived from certain mushrooms found in Mexico. Its effects are extremely close to those of LSD, as are mescaline and peyote. It is available in crystalline, powdered or liquid form.

DMT

Dimethyltryptamine is a more recent addition to the list of presently abused hallucinogenic agents. Although prepared synthetically, it is a natural constituent of the seeds of various West Indian and South American plants. "The businessman's trip" is how most people in the drug crowd describe DMT, because its effects are much more short-lived than LSD. Reduced dosages are reported to "turn on" a user for as little as thirty minutes. However, a normal dose provides a "trip" that often lasts for about six hours.

Morning Glory Seeds

Some varieties of morning glory seeds are also abused for their hallucinogenic effects. About one tenth as powerful as LSD, they can be chewed to obtain their effect on the mind. Like all other hallucinogens, however, their consumption is dangerous and can result in suidical reactions as well as certain physical discomforts.

NARCOTICS

Medically defined, narcotics are drugs which produce insensibility or stupor due to their depressant effect on the central nervous system. Included in this definition are opium and pain-killing drugs made from opium, for example, heroin, morphine, and codeine. Demerol® is an example of a synthetic man-made narcotic. Cocaine and marijuana are classified legally, but not chemically, as narcotic drugs. Natural and synthetic narcotics are the most effective pain killers in existence and are among the most valuable drugs available to the physician. They are widely used for short-term acute pain resulting from surgery, fractures, burns, and in the latter stages of terminal illness such as cancer.

Heroin

In the United States heroin is the illicit narcotic drug of most importance. By any of the names its users call it—*scag, smack, the big H, horse, junk, stuff, dope*—it is infamous as the hardest of drugs, the toughest of "monkeys" for anyone to get off his back. Heroin, a white powder made from morphine, is not used in any form of legal medical practice in this country. On heroin, the user usually progresses from "snorting" (inhaling the bitter powder like snuff) to "skin popping" (injecting the liquified drug just beneath the skin) to "mainlining" (injecting the drug directly into the bloodstream).

Heroin depresses the brain and results initially in a "rush" euphoric spasm of sixty seconds or so, accompanied by feelings of pleasure, strength, and superiority. These brief sensations are followed by a "high" which may last several hours. This state may be characterized by depression, lethargy, nervous apprehension, and reduction in hunger, thirst, and sex drive. The latter state can be relieved only by taking another "shot." Addiction to heroin can follow a single dose of the drug and almost invariably follows more than just a few doses. The intensity of withdrawal symptoms varies with the degree of physical dependence. This, in turn, is related to the amount of drug customarily used. Typically, the onset of symptoms occurs about eight to twelve hours after the last dose. These include shaking, sweating, chills, diarrhea, nausea, abdominal cramps, leg cramps, and mental anguish. Thereafter, symptoms increase in intensity, reach a peak between thirty-six and seventy-two hours, and then gradually diminish over the next five to ten days. However, weakness, insomnia, nervousness, and muscle aches and pains may persist for several weeks. In extreme cases, death may result.

Because increasing pressure by law enforcement authorities has made traffic in heroin more difficult, street supplies have tended to contain increasingly low percentages of active ingredient. The heroin content of a "bag" now ranges between three and ten percent. As a consequence, many present-day narcotic addicts experience mild withdrawal symptoms unless they are consuming many bags per day. On the other hand, narcotic addicts can die from overdosage when the supplies they buy on the street contain more than the customary low percentage of heroin.

Cocaine

Cocaine, made from the leaves of the coca bush found in certain South American countries, is an odorless, white crystalline powder with a bitter taste. "The leaf" or "snow" is either sniffed or injected directly into the vein. Unlike the other narcotics, cocaine is chemically classified as a stimulant. The stimulant effect of the drug results in excitability, talkativeness, and a relief of feelings of fatigue and hunger. Cocaine may produce a sense of euphoria, a sense of increased muscular strength, anxiety, fear, and hallucinations. Cocaine dilates the pupils and increases the heartbeat and blood pressure. Stimulation is followed by a period of depression. In overdosage, cocaine may so depress respiratory and heart function that death results. The intense stimulatory effects of cocaine usually result in the abuser voluntarily seeking sedation. This need for sedation has given rise to a practice of combining a depressant drug such as heroin with a drug such as cocaine (speedball) or alternating a drug such as cocaine with a depressant. Cocaine does not produce physical dependence. Tolerance does not develop and abusers seldom increase their customary dose. When drug supplies are cut off, the cocaine user does not experience withdrawal symptoms, but he does feel deeply depressed and hallucinations may persist for some time. Strong psychological dependence on the drug and a desire to reexperience the intense stimulation and hallucinations cocaine produces leads to its chronic misuse.

ORGANIC SOLVENTS

The organic solvents are volatile hydrocarbons such as airplane glue, gasoline, lighter fluid, ether, paint thinner, and aerosols. The inhalation of solvent fumes will produce a form of intoxication. The voluntary inhalation of these fumes is known as "sniffing." Inhalation is practiced most frequently by youngsters between ten and fifteen and occasionally up to eighteen years.

New glue usually is squeezed into a handkerchief or bag which is placed over the nose and mouth. Gasoline and paint thinner fumes may be inhaled directly from tanks and cars. After a number of "drags," the individual experiences excitation, exhilaration and excitement resembling the initial effects of alcoholic intoxication. Inhalation may be continued until the desired effects are achieved. The intoxication effects last for thirty to forty minutes, depending upon the amount inhaled. Blurring of vision, ringing ears, slurred speech, and staggering are common, as are hallucinations. The phase of intoxication is followed by drowsiness, stupor, and sometimes nausea. The user may even become unconscious for about an hour. Upon recovery, often there is no memory of this stage. Some persons learn to stay high for long periods of time by repeatedly sniffing at regular intervals.

Model airplane glue is probably the most widely abused of the solvents. Habitual users may use as many as five tubes of glue daily. The serious effects of glue sniffing involve toxic damage to the brain, kidneys, liver, and bone marrow. Additionally, a severe type of anemia has been observed in glue sniffers who have an inherited defect of the blood cells (sickle-cell disease). These are extremely serious consequences and may result in death. Reports of such tragedies are seen weekly in our newspapers.

Present knowledge concerning solvent inhalation indicates that physical dependence does not develop with the abuse of these agents, although a tendency to increase the amount inhaled suggests tolerance. Repeated use and relapse to use indicate the development of psychological dependence. The chief dangers of inhaling these substances are death by suffocation, the development of psychotic behavior, and the state of intoxication these substances produce.

Chapter III

HOW CAN YOU TELL IF YOUR CHILD IS TAKING DRUGS?

It is more important for the parent to know his child as opposed to a list of symptoms. If we know our children and there is an abrupt change in their behavior, then we know that something is wrong and determining the trouble becomes paramount.

As stated in previous chapters, the majority of what people think about drugs is false. The fact remains that the layman knows very little about the taking of drugs and the effect of drugs. A few years ago, most of the people who took drugs were from the slums and ghettos, but now all of a sudden the middle class children from the suburbs, small cities, and colleges are taking drugs and people are more concerned. Many children take the vicious drug heroin because they seek it and not because a pusher twists their arm and makes them take the first bag. They do not always suffer terrible kinds of agony and withdrawal pains from heroin that is heavily cut. Very often the withdrawal that most people think is so severe is not much rougher than a bad case of flu because the stuff has been cut so severely.

Many children sniff glue and move from glue to marijuana. They may even switch to Methedrine or speed. All of this may be done without the parents being aware that the child is taking drugs of any kind. Many children do not like "maining" because they do not like the disfigurement caused by the holes in the arms or other parts of the body. Some youths shoot between their toes or under their tongues to avoid visible signs of addiction. Most children are able to hide the "works," the needle and eyedropper with its top or spoon in order to mix the ingredients needed to shoot heroin. If the child wants to hide the works, then most parents will never find them.

In this day and time the chance of a child playing around with one drug or another is good and the chances are getting better. This does not mean that we have a whole generation of junkies in our society, but it does mean that many children from middle class, lower classes, and upper classes are experimenting with drugs. Many of these children do get hooked.

In some states the rate runs about 5 percent who use heroin. Better than 15 percent have tried LSD and 25 percent amphetamines. The most recent research indicates that the use of marijuana runs between 33 percent to 50 percent who try marijuana only once or twice but the percentage of children using marijuana regularly is much lower.

Once a child becomes addicted to the dreaded heroin, he is not generally waiting around in school but is out trying to find money to feed his habit. Often he is stealing. An addiction to heroin sometimes grows to a one-hundred dollar-a-day-habit and occasionally even more. Many children throughout the country are killed yearly by overdoses of heroin. Others die from hepatitis passed on by dirty needles. Some are even killed by policemen as they are shot when caught stealing or committing other crimes in order to get money for their habit.

Children from the middle class still prefer drugs other than heroin, such as LSD, marijuana, and speed. Heroin is feared by a majority of children from the upper classes but is still taken very much by the children in the lower classes.

Barbiturates are addicting and cause a very large percent of accidental deaths. Many children take the barbiturates at the same time that they are taking the amphetamines. This can be a deadly combination. Many children know that methedrine or speed will kill. This drug can bring on a psychosis which physicians claim is similar to schizophrenia. Some physicians state that the average life span of children who become addicted to methedrine is only five years after the onset of addiction.

When parents think that they can keep their children away from drugs which are dangerous, very often they are fooling themselves. If a child wants to go on a trip or turn on, he can do it with nutmeg, cleaning fluid, peyote, or even morning glory or marigold seeds. Children sniff glue to get high and have even tried Aerosol propellant which in some cases causes death.

The most common way that youngsters get high is from marijuana which is commonly called *pot, grass,* or *Mary Jane.* When kids smoke pot, they often burn incense or use some type of air sweetener to kill the smell. Young people who are high on marijuana also like to lie around and listen to loud music. Children often steal things around the house to sell in order to purchase a joint of marijuana which usually sells for about fifty cents per joint. From the argument standpoint, the best one that parents can use against marijuana is that it is illegal and can be responsible for sending a child to jail.

Unless the parent stumbles across his child when he is high, he may miss many of the symptoms of drug abuse. Much has been written about the symptoms of drug abuse, but the fact remains that drugs affect children in different ways. As already indicated, if a parent knows his child well, when the behavior becomes noticeably different, the parent knows that something is wrong. For example, after a shot of heroin the user proceeds from a state of euphoria to a kind of pleasant, warm glow. The individual may lose his appetite and complain of unspecific pains. This may or may not indicate to the parent that the child is high on heroin, but if this behavior persists, then certainly the parent knows that something is wrong.

A shot of LSD causes the child's pupils to enlarge. He often becomes nauseated, is flushed, and trembles a great deal. The palms of his hands sweat and his breath is irregular. If the parent should find his child in this state because of a dose of LSD, there is no telling what is going on inside the child's head. It probably is much more severe than the physical reactions.

If a parent observes a child who is taking barbiturates, then the child generally is sluggish, has slow speech, and seems to have very poor comprehension concerning what is said to him; therefore, the user has trouble remembering things. He is often sad and cries for no particular reason or he may laugh at a response which is not funny. The child or individual who uses amphetamines is jittery and perspires a great deal, talk inceasantly, and has difficulty sleeping. The child who sniffs glue has, as a rule of thumb, red eyes, an irritated nose, and feels ill a great deal of the time. The marijuana user may have reddened eyes and a dry mouth which a parent is not likely to detect, but even more noticeable, the child on marijuana has an unusual appetite for sweets. This may alert the parent that something unusual is going on, but at the same time many children have appetites for sweets when they are not doing anything wrong.

If the child is keeping peculiar hours and cannot account for his time, his school work has dropped considerably, has an increased thirst, his complexion has changed, his eyes are red much of the time, or he has lost interest in personal appearance and has chronic constipation, then the parent certainly is alerted that something is wrong. If the child has lost weight or is having trouble understanding directions, lost interest in school, then, of course, the parent knows that something is wrong. These are all signs of trouble, but they may not indicate that the child is doing anything wrong. But at the same time, parents cannot ignore the signs.

Parents should also be alerted to the fact that when a child develops a drug problem, this is not his only problem. A child who must resort to the psychological crutch of drugs has other problems dealing with personality, and the taking away of the drugs is not going to solve the personality problems. This is why the cure for drug addiction is so complex, because when we take away one psychological mechanism, then we must substitute another before the individual feels comfortable in society and can develop a healthy self-image. If we could all start off by having good, well-adjusted parents, then later, people would not need psychiatrists and psychologists, but the fact remains that not all children start off having wholesome home lives. Often, too, this is not the fault of the parent but is a situation over which they have no control. For example, during World War II many fathers did not see their children until the youngster was almost five years old. The major portion of the child's personality, in a case such as this, was formed by only one parent. This very often caused the child to develop feelings of insecurity and an inadequate self-image.

SYMPTOMS WHICH INDICATE WITHDRAWAL

When use of an addictive type drug, particularly heroin, has been interrupted the following are the easiest indicators for parents to spot: nervousness, restlessness, sweating, yawning, running eyes and nose, twitching, vomiting, cramps, pupils wide open, and diarrhea.

WHAT PARENTS CAN DO

Many parents believe that if their child tries marijuana once he is sure to go on to heroin or become an "acid head." This is simply not true; therefore, the first thing that parents should realize is that one experiment with marijuana or other drugs is not a sure step into deep trouble for their child. Too often, parents become overly alarmed about drugs and have even had their teenage youngster arrested for having smoked marijuana just a few times. Having mentioned these things, it is important to admonish that the parents' first concern is to "keep their cool." They should not blow their stack so to speak, threaten to call the police, monitor telephone conversations, and spy on the youngsters. These things merely make the youths resent the parents even more, and these scare techniques are seldom helpful. The scare approach tells only one side of the story, and many youngsters have seen their friends using drugs and know that their friends have not gotten into trouble and are able to function fairly well in society. The youth of today resents being told only one side of the story and cannot see the difference between smoking pot, for example, and parents using cigarettes and alcohol. Therefore, again it must be stressed that parents should "keep their cool." They should have information concerning drugs, whereby they can intelligently talk with their children and share with them the facts about drugs.

If the parent discovers that the child is definitely taking drugs, he should be firm but fair in the discipline. If he finally becomes convinced that his child is hooked on drugs, then in all probability the parents need outside help. They should seek that outside help as fast as possible. Too often in affluent families, the last person that youngsters in trouble turn to is the parent. They have had experiences with the parents most of their lives and know the reaction to getting in trouble; the screams of the parents are familiar. Many, many parents who really care about their youngsters cannot transmit this fact. Children are quick to recognize when parents are overanxious and when they are extremely disturbed about a situation. Therefore, if we approach the solution to the drug problem with hysteria and tell the youth that he is a taint on the family, then of course, we run the risk of increasing our troubles rather than minimizing them.

There are many slang terms which drug abusers and drug pushers use, and these terms become a secret language. If parents become familiar with these terms, it would greatly enhance their chances of discovering drug abuse by their children and their children's friends. The following pages describe slang terms used by drug abusers and drug pushers.

SLANG TERMS

Acid—LSD
Acid head—an abuser of LSD
Artillery—equipment for injecting drugs
Bag—a container of drugs
Bagman—a drug supplier
Bang—narcotic injection
Barbs—barbiturates
Bennies—Benzedrine (amphetamine sulfate)
Bernice—cocaine
Big D—LSD
Big John—the police
Blanks—poor quality narcotics
Blasted—under the influence of drugs
Blow a stick—to smoke a marijuana cigarette
Blow your mind—enter into a frenzied state of mind
Blue acid—LSD
Blue devils—Amytal (amobarbital)
Blue heavens—Amytal
Blue velvet—paregoric and an antihistamine

Bombido—injectable amphetamine
Boy—heroin
Bread—money
Bull—a Federal narcotic agent, a police officer
Burned—to receive phony or badly diluted drugs
Busted—arrested
Buzz—feeling of exhilaration produced by a drug
Cactus—mescaline
Candy—barbiturates
Champ—drug abuser who will not reveal his supplier—even under
    pressure
Charge—marijuana
Charged up—under the influence of drugs
Charlie—cocaine
Chief—marijuana
Chipping—taking small amounts of drugs on an irregular basis
Clear up—to withdraw from drugs
Coasting—under the influence of drugs
Coke—cocaine
Cold turkey—sudden drug withdrawal
Connect—to purchase drugs
Cook up a pill—to prepare opium for smoking
Co-pilots—amphetamine tablets
Corine—cocaine
Crystal—methedrine crystal
Cut—to adulterate a narcotic by adding milk-sugar
Dealer—a drug supplier
Dexies—Dexedrine (dextroamphetamine sulfate)
Dime bag—a ten-dollar purchase of narcotics
Dollies—Dolophine® (methadone hydrochloride)
Dominoes—Durophet (amphetamine/sedative)
Double trouble—tuinal
Down—heavily addicted
Dust—cocaine
Fix—an injection of narcotics
Flake—cocaine
Footballs—oval-shaped amphetamine sulfate tablets

Fuzz—the police
Gage—marijuana
Gee-head—paregoric abuser
Girl—cocaine
Gold dust—cocaine
Goofballs—barbiturates
Gow—heroin
Gow-head—an opium addict
Grass—marijuana
Griefo—marijuana
H—heroin
Hard stuff—morphine, cocaine, or heroin
Harry—heroin
Hash—marijuana
Hawk—LSD
Hay—marijuana
Hearts—Benzedrine or Dexedrine (amphetamine sulfate and
            dextroamphetamine sulfate)
Heavy—heroin
Hemp—marijuana
Hooked—addicted
Hophead—narcotic addict
Horse—heroin
Hung up—unable to obtain drugs; depressed and let down
Hype—narcotic addict
Ice cream habit—a small, irregular drug habit
Instant Zen—LSD
Jack—a heroin tablet
Jelly babies—amphetamine-type pills
Jive—marijuana
Joint—a marijuana cigarette
Joy popping—taking heroin occasionally
Joy powder—heroin
Joystick—marijuana-type cigarette
Junkie—a narcotic addict
Kick—thrill
Lipton tea—poor quality narcotics

Locoweed—marijuana
Machine—syringe
Mainline—to inject drugs directly into a vein
Man—the police
Manicure—high-grade marijuana
Mary Jane—marijuana
Medicine—heroin
Meth—methamphetamine
Mezz—marijuana
Mickey Finn—chloral hydrate
Minstrel—Durophet
Miss Emma—morphine
Monkey—a drug habit where physical dependence is present
Mor a grifa—marijuana
Mud—crude opium
Mutah—marijuana
Nickel bag—a five dollar purchase of narcotics
Nimby—nembutal
On the nod—under the influence of drugs
Oranges—dexedrine
Paper—a prescription or packet of narcotics
Peaches—benzedrine
Peanuts—barbiturates
Pep pills—amphetamines
Peyote—mescaline
Pierce—a container of drugs
Pinks—seconal
Pop—inject
Pot—marijuana
Quill—a folded matchbox cover from which narcotics are sniffed
    through the nose
Rainbows—tuinal
Reader—a prescription
Red devils—seconal
Reds—seconal
Reefer—marijuana cigarette
Roach—the butt of a marijuana cigarette

Rope—marijuana
Roses—benzedrine
Salt—powdered heroin
Sam—Federal narcotic agent
Satch cotton—cotton used to strain narcotics before injection
Scat—heroin
Scene—group of users of drugs
Scratching—to obtain drugs
Seggy—seconal
Shot—injected intravenously
Slammed—in jail
Sleepers—barbiturates
Smack—heroin
Snort—take drugs nasally by sniffing
Snow—cocaine
Solid—marijuana and tobacco cigarette
Speed—methamphetamine
Spliff—marijuana cigarette
Stick—marijuana
Stuff—heroin
Sweets—amphetamine-type pills
Tea—marijuana
Texas tea—marijuana
Tooies—tuinal
Truck drivers—amphetamine
Uncle—Federal narcotic agent
User—taker of drugs
Wake-ups—amphetamine
Weed—marijuana
Whites—amphetamines; benzedrine
White stuff—morphine
Yellow—nembutal
Yellow jackets—nembutal

Chapter IV

TREATMENT OF DRUG ABUSERS

As mentioned in earlier chapters there is considerable concern today for the young drug abusers. The young person's needs are inevitably complex, especially in the context of life's problems and drug abuse. The adolescent normally strives for independence in terms of the demands of society, parental pressures, and his own personal goals. Drug abuse is a manifestation of his ambivalent feelings and is a crutch which helps him avoid some of his conflicts. Feelings of fear, anger, frustration, and depression often lead one to seek gratification in alcohol and/or drugs. The individual's feelings expressed in this manner present a challenge to the medical and nursing professions, psychology, education, and to society as a whole in terms of treatment.

It has been alluded to in previous chapters that the word *drug* is now widely used to mean those compounds which are taken for pleasure rather than for therapeutic purposes. Compounds used to treat illness, such as digitalis or aspirin, are now called medicines.

MEDICAL TREATMENT

Drug abuse presents many problems to the medical profession. These problems range from keeping detailed records for dangerous drugs to the complex problems of treating the drug user, either for intoxication or for long-range cure. Very often physicians must treat side effects of drug abuse and illnesses which are closely related, such as infectious hepatitis. To some this problem is new but physicians have long been concerned about the human suffering, disability, death, and social disruption resulting from drug abuse.

ACUTE TOXICITY

There is an ever-increasing problem in the hospital emergency room concerning the treatment of drug intoxication, which may range from mild agitation and acute anxiety to full-blown mental illness. Many of these patients can be handled adequately with mild tranquilizers and nonthreatening techniques. Physicians tell us that the hospital personnel should avoid displaying hostility. It would be an understatement to say that it is extremely difficult for people to be nonchalant and calm in a situation whereby some hostile, drug-crazed youth is tearing apart the hospital facilities, striking the nurses violently, and generally disturbing everybody in sight.

After the symptoms of panic have subsided many of these patients can be sent home but some will need hospitalization for the administration of oxygen, observation, and medical treatment of convulsions.

Marijuana appears relatively harmless, and acute reactions seldom need treating. When a panic reaction does occur, pot users can be usually treated with mild tranquilizers.

While a casual marijuana user may not be emotionally disturbed, for any youth involved in anything more serious than passing experimentation, drug use can be extremely hazardous. The teen-age period of life is a very important phase of biological, social, intellectual, and personality development. Drugs which interfere with the youngster's judgment and his sense of personal and social responsibility before he fully matures carry a heavy risk of personal and social disturbance. While the treatment of marijuana abuse is not difficult, it is the responsibility of the physician to recommend counseling for the youth in order that he may find a better method of solving his problems.

HALLUCINOGENS

Hallucinogens have previously been discussed and the best known are LSD, mescaline, and peyote. The physician may be called for treatment after a "bad trip." The medical management consists of reassurance, reduction of external stimuli, and relief of the panic with medications.

The reactions of the hospital personnel are very important in the successful treatment of a "bad trip." In mild cases of anxiety and agitation, a sympathetic attitude and talking to the patient concerning his fears may comprise successful treatment. In situations other than very mild cases, the "trip" should be terminated chemically as quickly as possible. This immediate termination greatly reduces the incidence of flashes in the future and also sedates a patient who is potentially destructive.

If you are a careful reader you know by now that the amphetamines are known as the *pep pills* and are a much abused group of drugs. They perhaps are the most widely abused because they are extremely easy to get from drugstores. Men and women take them daily to combat obesity, college kids take them at exam time, and truck drivers take them to combat sleepiness.

Acute agitation, hyperactivity, and insomnia may result from the use of these drugs. Precipitous withdrawal of the stimulation may occur; and the truck driver suddenly slumps at the wheel causing a wreck; or the college student who has stayed awake all night collapses while taking the examination; or the housewife suddenly faints. The medical profession tells us that amphetamines are harmful in their physiologic effects and in their histologic damage to body cells. Treatment is with sedation and in some cases hospitalization is needed.

The management of acute toxicity in the young drug user is an important phase of medical practice today, but it is far from an easy phase.

REMEDIAL TREATMENT

The drug user returns repeatedly to the hospital emergency room for acute care unless something is done to help him develop better mechanisms. The family physician often is called upon to deal with this serious problem. His first attempt usually is to diagnose the underlying conditions which led to the drug problem. These patients may be classified as social, neurotic, or psychotic drug takers.

Social drug taking, especially of marijuana, occurs widely today among dissatisfied youths who are insecure and who feel rejected, and by those seeking group conformity and pleasure. Neurotic drug abuse, like other signs of neurotic behavior occurs as an attempt to relieve anxiety and frustration. The danger is addiction and the treatment is psychological in nature. Psychotic drug abuse is caused when the normal and neurotic mechanisms are rendered useless because the mental illness is precipitated by drugs. The danger is violence; the treatment is medical and psychological. Naturally, in our society there are mixed types of drug users.

Physicians tell us that classification is very important because management is distinctly different for the three types.

Social Drug Abuse

In some college communities today taking drugs is so prevalent that those who do not may be looked upon as "square." The young person is generally more concerned about pleasing his peers than pleasing his parents.

Often too the parents need psychiatric attention. They can be helped to see that the youth must be allowed to make his own decisions and he must live with his life which results from these decisions. Parents have the right to counsel their children, but this must be tempered with gentleness. They must also realize that they are not professional counselors. They must continue their moral support with the conviction that today's fads like all other fads will run their course. Remember the raccoon coats and goldfish swallowing of the 1920 era. Youths do not do these things today but the fads are similar in that they serve a purpose in the life of the young person.

Of course drugs are much more dangerous than other fads which have come and gone, but severe punishment often aggravates the situation. Some sound principles of management in the social abuse deal with tolerance, patience, love, confidence, gentle pressure, and a sense of humor. The total situation is more important than the isolated problem. If we can learn to manage the total situation adequately then the specific problem can be solved.

Neurotic Drug Abuse

The neurotic cannot use defense mechanisms properly and, in the face of severe stress, resorts to unhealthy neurotic mechanisms. They frequently have a low stress-tolerance and become anxious and fearful when confronted with conflict and frustration. They are often tense, irritable, and unhappy; and because they cannot be resolved through healthy mechanisms, these conditions lead to psychological and physical problems.

Defense Mechanisms

The defense mechanisms are learned to protect and enhance the organism. They are called into play when we find ourselves in a position which threatens the ego. These mechanisms help us to soften disappointment, alleviate anxiety, protect ourselves against trauma, and to maintain our feelings of worth and adequacy.

We must consider them normal reactions unless they are carried to an extreme. They can have certain drawbacks, with self-deception and distortion of reality being the two chief ones. They operate on a relatively unconscious level and are not subject to normal checks—as a matter of fact, people resent being told that they are using a defense mechanism.

The more common defense mechanisms are as follows:

Fantasy—Gratifying frustration in imaginary achievements.

Rationalization—Attempting to prove that one's behavior is rational and justifiable by making excuses.

Projection—Placing blame for difficulties upon others.

Repression—Keeping painful or dangerous thoughts at the unconscious level.

Regression—Retreating to stages and actions involving less mature responses (childlike).

Identification—Increasing feelings of worth by identifying self with a person who is outstanding.

Compensation—Covering up weaknesses by emphasizing desirable traits.

Displacement—Discharging hostility on less dangerous objects (hitting the wall).

Besides the thrill-seekers, the largest number of drug abusers are probably neurotics. Most are plagued by inferior feelings, and many feel quite insecure. Regarding the young neurotic drug taker, treatment, at first, is aimed at the patient and not at his parents. It is important to find out about his total present situation: scholastic, extracurricular, social, and medical condition. Later, his parents will be brought into the picture and therapy sessions will involve parents and youth.

The first step is to help the patient see that his problems are not only due to the present environment but also to inner conflicts. The therapist may use a nondirective approach (reflects what the patient says) or a directive approach (leads, guides, and interprets).

Psychotic Drug Abuse

In psychotic disorders (mental illness) the person displays a severe personality breakdown, usually with a marked distortion of reality, and often with loss of contact with reality. Psychotic disorders are divided into two categories—functional and organic—because the condition may arise from psychological or organic causes or a combination of the two. The functional psychoses are divided into four types as follows:

1. Schizophrenic
2. Paranoid reactions
3. Mood fluctuations
4. Senile psychosis

The schizophrenic retreats from reality and there is usually a disintegration of the personality. Delusions (false beliefs) and hallucinations (seeing and hearing things) are common. In paranoid reaction the person maintains an intact personality but has delusions of grandeur or persecution or both. The individual suffering from mood reactions has disturbances of mood. He has severe fluctuations in mood ranging from extreme elation to severe depression. He may also display disturbances of thought patterns along with depression. Senile psychosis occurs generally in later life and would not pertain to most drug users. The senile period is usually considered to be from forty to sixty-five years.

The use of drugs, including marijuana, has been the precipitating cause of mental illness in many instances. The psychosis is usually acute but may be chronic and last for many months or several years.

The treatment involves the use of medicines such as pheno-thiazines and antidepressants, electroshock therapy (for depressed patients), hospitalization, and psychotherapy, which is primarily supportive in nature.

THE PSYCHIATRIST

A great deal of controversy stems around the referral of a youth by a family physician to a psychiatrist. Naturally, the answer depends on the physician, patient, and the availability of psychiatrists in the area. It is a fact that in America we do not have enough psychiatrists to treat all drug addicts. Drug addiction is on the increase; therefore, the problem will become more acute as time passes. The family physician who knows the situation will refer a patient to a psychiatrist if the need arises. For example, the family physician will usually refer the drug abuser who is psychotic for immediate psychiatric treatment and hospitalization.

TREATMENT FOR HEROIN ABUSERS

The first thing that should be emphasized concerning treatment for heroin addiction is that no one approach works in all cases. In all probability there are approximately as many approaches as experts.

British System

The British system operates from the viewpoint that heroin abusers are sick and not really committing a crime. The majority of British physicians seem to think that complete withdrawal is a danger physically and psychologically; therefore, the British physicians at one time were allowed to make the drug available to the abusers. Naturally, this eliminated the bulk of pushers and black-market supply. Another important feature was that it made it unnecessary for the abuser to steal in order to supply the habit.

The British law led to an addict registration but did not cure the patient. However, most research indicates that only a small percentage of heroin abusers are permanently cured. The

British found, too, that some physicians overprescribed heroin to the abusers, and the abusers sold what they did not need. Because of this reason, in 1968 the British government specified certain consultants at certain hospitals to prescribe drugs.

Methadone Program

Drs. Vincent Dole and Marie Nyswonder pioneered this approach in 1964 in the state of New York. In this method the abuser is switched from heroin to methadone which is a synthetic substitute. Methadone can be made available to the abuser for about fifteen cents a day. The program pioneered by these two physicians also includes therapy along with the methadone maintenance program. This program allows the abuser to work instead of constantly having to steal to supply a daily dosage from five dollars to fifty dollars or even more.

The physicians who advocate the use of methadone insist that this treatment is no worse than the treatment utilized by a diabetic when he takes a daily injection of insulin.

Many physicians and attorneys object to substituting one addiction for another. A survey, though, of the addict in the program found that they are totally in support of the treatment. Many of them stated that it is the only way for leading a normal life.

The most accepted program for dealing with the drug abuser is the utilizing of a small therapeutic community. The physicians detoxify the patient and they, psychologist and social workers, attempt to rehabilitate him through therapy. Many former addicts work at these controlled therapeutic stations. Many half-way houses exist as a place where addicts can live while they are being rehabilitated. Two federal narcotic houses, one in Lexington, Kentucky and the other in Fort Worth, Texas, serve mostly patients who are ordered there by the courts. Research indicates that better than 90 percent of the patients in the federal hospitals once released return to the use of heroin.

Some of the half-way houses rely heavily on abusers and ex-abusers to help one another. This is a type of group therapy and is done under staff supervision. Many of the programs run from two to three years.

It is a fact that many addicts who leave the hospitals and communities return to narcotics. It is also true as stated earlier that there is no agreement among physicians as to which approach is best.

Research indicates that if children are already taking drugs, education programs in the school are of no use. The youth who is an abuser can watch a movie over and over but to no avail. The residential group therapy center seems to provide the strongest help for the addict. In all probability this residential center type of treatment, coupled with a synthetic drug program is the best treatment for the dope addict.

Chapter V

THE ROLE OF PARENTS AND TEACHERS IN DRUG EDUCATION

THE ROLE OF PARENTS

The parent has an especially important role in the prevention of drug abuse. Certainly our schools, churches, and community agencies and groups have the responsibility of influencing drug education programs and parents should encourage these institutions and groups to develop programs which teach respect for drugs and which also teach about drug abuse. Parents should certainly work in and with these groups; yet their role extends even beyond this involvement for a child's attitudes and outlook on life is learned primarily in the home. The parent therefore has an influence in his family that no other person can have. The parent must work to make this influence a *positive* rather than a negative one.

Drug respect begins with the home medicine cabinet. We must teach our children respect for all kinds of drugs, even aspirin; this education begins with our young preschoolers. We should point out that drugs have a very important use in our lives, and that when we are sick they are most important. We should teach them to take drugs if they are needed, and to follow directions explicitly. When the parent takes medication, it is a good policy to explain to the child what it is and its purposes. As parents we must be positive examples of the proper use of drugs. We can tell a child he should never take medicines of others or take unprescribed samples. Yet if he sees his parent taking Aunt Sally's prescribed medication for a sinus headache or gladly accepting drug samples from the neighbor who works in a clinic or hospital, then our work will have no meaning. Drug education by the parent is imperative for young children, and this early education of drugs can carry over into adolescent and teen years.

As children grow older, the drug abuse problem should

45

be discussed between parents and children; meal time is a particularly appropriate time and setting. Articles relating to drug abuse should be read and discussed by the family members. Penalties under the law should be discussed but not harped on. Strict legislation to control drugs is not the answer to prevention of drug abuse. Only education will save the life or the healthy brain of a child tempted to experiment.

The fallacies, as well as the facts, of drugs and drug abuse should not be ignored. Children and youth need to know more than one side of the total story, since much of their information has come from their peer groups. Thus, the parents have the obligation to be intelligently and accurately informed about the use and misuse of drugs. Scare tactics will not be effective. One father said he thought the best way of steering children away from drugs is "to scare the hell out of them." Such an approach will provide the child with biased information, or half-truths, and the child will sooner or later "find you out." The youth of today are bright and they can make decisions; therefore, we must give them good intelligent information and let them make their own decision regarding their position on drug abuse.

In the family the fact should be discussed that our needs which are met and partially fulfilled by drug dependence can be satisfied in many other ways. A person can feel good without drinking, and a person can feel good without taking drugs. It is not enough to tell children these things; our lives must exemplify these truths.

One physician quoted a remark made by one of his youthful patients, "I don't know why my folks get so excited when I use drugs. My Dad's been hung up on Bourbon and water for years, and my mother smokes two packs of cigarettes a day." If children and youth see their parents overindulge in alcohol and tobacco over a period of years, it is very difficult to make them see that using drugs is wrong. If parents cannot defend their lives and values, how can they expect children to respect them and not know that they are hypocritical. We must give our children a healthy, wholesome model early in life to follow.

If this is done, then in all probability, the child will not resort to a psychological crutch such as drugs.

Children and youths do not dress and act the way their parents do. Many parents tend to remember education and the way they dress as being the only way. We tend to look at too many things through our own eyes, and this very often causes the "generation gap." Children like and must dress the way their peers dress. They must look and act like their peers in order to have peer acceptance. If the peers seem "far out" to parents there is the possibility the parents should look around to see how all children are acting and dressing. If they are depriving their children of being similar to other children, they are making a mistake. Such a mistake can lead a child to a psychological crutch. That crutch could be drugs.

Each member of the family should be cognizant of the fact that if any member gets to the point that he cannot function adequately without a psychological crutch, then he should go to a psychologist or psychiatrist for help. The other members of his family should be willing to engage in psychotherapy with him and be supportive and accepting of him. Concerning the psychiatrist, though, we should be aware that we are not replacing the woodshed with the couch. Many parents and children need psychiatric help, but many do not. Many children need firm punishment and discipline. Some young persons, who have become addicted to heroin, say they think they would not have done so if their parents had been really concerned about them, and also had set strict standards. Yet discipline must be firm—and fair. Youths want authority, not tyranny.

Children and youth need privacy and should be allowed to keep diaries and expect their telephone conversations to be private. Parents should not become substitute policemen and should not harass their children by going around searching their rooms, going through the pockets of their clothes, and interrogating the child like a policeman. Parental blessings should not be given to children without careful consideration. The child or youth should know when he asks his parents' permission to do something that he has all the facts to present to the parents because past performance by parents would indicate that he is allowed to participate in various activities if it appears to be in his best interest.

It is interesting and alarming that in families where youths are abusing drugs, there seems to be terrible chasms between parents and children. Parents of these youths often reject their children and attempt to impose their values on their children in an overbearing and self-righteous way. Investigators indicate that most runaway children are actually "pushed away."

Thus the role of the parent in the prevention of drug abuse is little different from another role—that of parenthood. If a parent assumes his role of parenthood responsibly and intelligently, his part in the drug education of his child will evolve naturally out of the greater responsibility of rearing the child in the best way possible.

THE ROLE OF TEACHERS

The drug abuse problem is certainly national in scope; yet it is not a national problem as much as it is a local problem—in the community, the school, and the home. Thus, here is the place where education has got to be done. The school, the parents, the church, and the community agencies must work together to curb the growing problem of drug abuse.

The schools should not wait for community groups and agencies to invite their support in their attack on drug abuse. School administrators and teachers in every community must rapidly become thoroughly informed with the complex problem of drug abuse and must accept a serious and immediate responsibility for attacking it with thoughtful and effective measures.

School administrators and teachers may be reluctant to initiate a drug education program because they believe that such an effort may serve primarily to stimulate interest where no interest exists. Yet others feel that in an area of belief or behavior where the young person may be subjected to pressures to do something about which he is unsure, some reliable information is better than none. Also, recent research has shown that drug education has had some very positive effects even in the ghettos.

Control studies indicate that disadvantaged youngsters who have had meaningful experiences with the dangers of addiction are fearful of and reluctant to try heroin. Repeatedly, drug abusers have stated that they might not have become involved if they had had factual information beforehand, particularly in cases where thrill seeking and curiosity were the apparent main motives for experimenting with drugs in the first place. Likewise, research has shown that young people smoke marijuana because of a *lack* of adequate educational programs on the subject. Thus, these facts explicitly demonstrate the need for programs of drug education in the school, programs aimed at both the youth and their parents.

There are no simple formulas for effective drug education programs. What any school does will and should depend on its educational goals, the emphasis it puts on the personal and social growth of students, its typical manner of working with students both in and out of the classroom, and the characteristics of its student body. Each school must shape its own program in light of these factors. There are, however, certain general principles which should be considered.

The emphasis of the drug education program should be on individual attitudes and needs, societal values, changing styles of life, and implications for the future. The task of the school is not necessarily to educate about the evils and dangers of drug abuse but rather to educate about the human personality, about chemicals and how they interact with people, about social control, about the positive and negative consequences of drug use for the individual and society. It is imperative that students think through the issues regarding the personal and societal meaning of drug use. For example, for the affluent individual from the middle or upper class, drugs serve as a means to immediate pleasure and gratification. While for the disadvantaged individual from the lower socioeconomic class, drugs serve as an escape from his deplorable social condition. Thus an educational approach should give information and provide opportunity for discussion of the many relevant social issues as well as other ways of fulfilling individual needs which are partially satisfied by drug use.

Too often, use of sensational accounts of drug users or "scare" tactics are used in drug education programs. Such techniques are usually ineffective because the teenager's direct knowledge frequently contradicts them. Today's youth are demanding—and are entitled to—accurate, factual, unprejudiced information. Given the facts honestly and directly, they respond quickly and sensibly. For example, the apparent decline in the use of LSD is believed to be related to the well-published reports of possible adverse psychological and potential biological hazards. Thus an objective view of drug use and abuse must be presented.

Discussion must be limited to the dangers of the negative side. The facts as well as the fantasies and uncertainties about drugs and drug use should be presented. Topics such as the personal meaning in taking drugs, implications for one's life style, interpersonal relationships, and future goals should be explored. To be effective, prevention ultimately must be based on each individual's decision not to use drugs because they are incompatible with his personal goals.

Teachers should avoid being moralistic and judgmental when talking about drugs and drug users. In this day and age the teacher cannot afford to become a preacher. Today information about drugs, politics, sex, racial and social equality, and international affairs is disseminated by a variety of media—only one of these being the classroom teacher. The teacher is no longer the indisputable authority and "preaching" or "talking down" to students will result in the teachings being ignored. The teacher must take a flexible approach maintaining an open mind to the range of student feelings and attitudes.

The teacher should work diligently to keep lines of communication open. The student must feel free to express his views and discuss his concerns. As pointed out earlier, *both sides of the issue should be discussed,* all the while the teacher is encouraging the students to question, to search and weigh evidence, and to arrive at a logical conclusion or position based on factual, accurate information. Rejecting a student's views or points may serve to alter his classroom verbal behavior but it is unlikely to change his thinking. The teacher should take care not to regard himself as the only teacher in the room. Much is to be learned from students—their knowledge of drug abuse, their feelings and attitudes.

It is important that young people be aware of the possible long-term results of their behavior in regard to the law. Persons using or possessing certain drugs risk the chance of a jail term. For example, possession of marijuana for personal use is a felony. Conviction means a sentence of not less than two years and not more than ten for the first offense. Conviction of a felony means loss of voting rights and many times hinders an individual from securing employment. While this should not be the primary emphasis, the legal implications should be discussed as factors to be taken into consideration in any decision to use or not to use drugs. The fact that the abuse of drugs frequently carries with it heavy legal penalities should not be dismissed lightly.

Sometimes a student-run discussion on the prevention of drug abuse may be especially effective. Teen-agers are particularly susceptible to the power of group approval; identification and belongingness are tremendous motivating factors for their behavior. Thus, a major influence on an individual's use of drugs is the peer group, or his associates. Certainly student-led discussions might be more effective than adult-directed, in light of these facts. Or former drug abusers might be effective in communicating with students, for they can "tell it like it is."

The presentation of the basic facts of the drug problem and the particular abusable drugs could be part of a regular course. An introductory biology or psychology course would be very appropriate. Likewise, a social studies class would be suitable, as drug abuse certainly influences the structure of society. It is important, however, not to limit study of drug abuse to a specific drug abuse unit or lecture. Whenever possible, information and discussions regarding drug abuse should be integrated into the general curriculum.

There are many excellent films, pamphlets, books, and other materials which could be used in a drug education program.

Nearby colleges or universities may be of help in such a program. In a few states, colleges and universities offer traveling programs for junior and senior high school students. Such materials and resources are good but should be used as a springboard to effective *discussion* by the students, their parents, and other concerned adults.

Teachers can also serve to demonstrate that it is possible to live an involved, meaningful life without the use of drugs to add excitement or meaning. Too often abuse of alcohol and tobacco on the part of adults is the thrust of the students' argument in favor of marijuana. The adult who is himself "turned on" by life without recourse to drugs is one of the best advertisements for that type of life. The teacher must help students find other ways of fulfilling the needs which they feel are, or could be, met by drug use. The teacher may open up, for individual or classroom discussion, ways in which students are or can become involved in activities that have personal meaning for them.

Many young people today feel strongly about problems of our contemporary world, and opportunities for active involvement might be encouraged. Some might find meaning in a program for disadvantaged children, or as a volunteer in a hospital, or working for political candidates. While a strong interest in other activities may not deter a student from experimenting with drugs, he is less likely to adopt habitual drug use if he feels "turned on" by shared and constructive human experiences.

Adolescence is a lonely time for many teenagers. The young person who has personality problems sometimes turns to drug use as a means of finding a kind of group acceptance. The student who is having more than the usual difficulties in finding his place in some orthodox group will sometimes respond very well to a special interest shown by one of his teachers. Even when the teacher is unable to help him solve a problem, he may direct the student to needed professional help. Particularly for the student with a poor home situation, a sympathetic teacher can provide a model of an understanding adult who has no need to escape into a state of drugged unreality.

Finally, it is the individual who must decide for himself whether or not to use drugs. No authority, whether school official or police officer, can make that decision for him. Yet it is the challenge of the school, home, church, and community to help the young person to clarify his personal responsibility and to make an informed and intelligent decision.

SECTION II

This section deals with the attitudes and knowledge of professional people, parents, and children concerning drug abuse. To obtain this information, policemen were interviewed as were ministers, teachers, parents, school administrators, and one college student whose father was a drug addict and died from an overdose of drugs.

This section is included because many people having drug abuse problems have confrontations with police, counsel with ministers, have contact with teachers and school administrators, and are concerned parents and children.

These interviews indicate that the people dealing with individuals having a drug problem are not only informed about drugs and drug abuse but are also concerned about the problem. Of major concern is the fact that we are a "pill taking" nation. Children grow up seeing the medicine cabinet opened daily and pill after pill being swallowed by parents and forced down the throats of gagging children. The gagging child, after taking so many pills, finally becomes acclimated to the situation.

The school people are particularly concerned because they see bright-eyed children who are making good grades become dull-eyed children who are failing. School administrators are concerned because of the disrupting effect that drugs have on children. Ministers are concerned because the lives of the members of their congregation are being disrupted and the families are being torn apart. The parent who wrote about his son is not only concerned about his son's health but because he and his wife did not observe the symptoms of drug addiction. Lastly, the student whose father was a drug addict is concerned about drugs affecting all members of the family because she knows from experience.

Chapter VI

A TEACHER LOOKS AT DRUG ABUSE IN THE SCHOOLS

VERNON E. LEWIS*

The boys in my classes are changing: they are growing taller, getting heavier, talking "hipper"; and they are filled with a nameless terror of—and rage at—the city streets.

I always strive to understand their moods of restlessness— and their passions for life—since I, too, grew up in the city and know the ways of the city. Indeed, their life-style, their frames of references are comprehensible phenomena to me. As a teacher I possess special attitudes which these bewildered, outraged boys may find utterly appalling and intimidating. On the other hand, as a teacher, I have to show these students their vast potentials as citizens and future parents and leaders.

The terrible and murderous power of drugs is rampant in many areas of our society, and I feel that drugs can bring an inevitable doom upon many of our youngsters in school.

I daily marvel at these youths, their innocence and their astonishment that life often contains contradictions: the thrill of heroin versus the deadly overdose; the ecstasy of LSD versus the death-dealing hot shot. During recess I see how the boys loiter together; they laugh and talk, exchanging jokes, telling the most fantastic and improbable tall tales about their adventures in the streets. When the bell rings, they return to their classes, many of them filled with a false power and ridiculous assumptions about their lives. But many youths in our society have succumbed to drug addiction and will never return to classes (their names are listed in the obituary columns or in the files of asylums). They are the ones who perished, raging and gasping and crying for the quick fix of the needle.

---

*The experiences related by Vernon E. Lewis, a teacher in the Little Rock public school system, were not a part of the Little Rock school system but an inter-school in a large city.

Sometimes, in the evenings, when the last bell rings, I sit at my desk, glad to be alone, remembering the unspeakable dread in the eyes and laughter of the boys on the playground. Lost hope, I have learned, can lead the boys to robbing service stations and muggings—anything to get enough money to purchase drugs, to keep "the monkey" off their backs and—for a brief period—not to be terrified of the impending darkness.

Often, at school, they fight desperately for self-control, trying not to nod as the drugs capture their consciousness; they do not want me to learn of their predicament and terror. The other teachers at school are disturbed at the drug problem, too. They lecture about punishment and safety, but they have powerful competition from the drug pushers and hustlers in the dazzling, brutal streets.

I have learned, too, that there are ample drugs for the addict— as long as he has money to pay for them. Imagine a teen-age boy selling drugs to an adolescent girl, who recently became a prostitute, in order to pay for her drug habit! I have learned, moreover, not to shove a youth into a corner and ask him, point-blank, if he is using drugs. Sooner or later, a boy or girl will approach me and tell me about someone who is on drugs.

Imagine the crazed voice and tense bewilderment of a boy, high on drugs, stealing money from a teacher's purse, cursing the teacher, threatening to assault her, and stalking out of the classroom. One boy was found dead, in a telephone booth, with a hypodermic needle stuck in his arm. His parents were shocked when they learned that he was a drug addict. A young girl was killed when her boy friend stabbed her in the heart with an ice pick, as they argued over who was to turn on first with some marijuana they had purchased from a pusher on a street corner.

Another youth, K, whom I had taught in a couple of my classes and whom I had watched grow, in a couple of years, into a tall, strapping boy, was always in some kind of trouble with the teachers and with his classmates. He seemed to have a knack for getting into trouble—serious trouble. And he did not seem to care. During the lunch break, he would go home and sometimes stay, but often he would return to school in a very belligerent mood. There never was a smell of alcohol on his breath but during these times he seemed to be in a stupor, a sort of ecstatic limbo.

One day during the lunch period, I saw him and a much older boy together on a street corner near the school. They were walking toward the nearby business district, which was in the opposite direction of K's home. In a few minutes, they disappeared around the corner. When the bell rang for the next class, K had returned to school talking with a couple of youths on his way to class. I watched him walk jauntily into the school building, his hands in his pockets. Five or ten minutes later, as the students in my class were working on an assignment, I heard a girl shriek. K was standing near the girl. She was crying and calling for me. K stood stonily, staring vacantly at me, yelling that the girl was picking on him and telling lies on him. I told K to return to his desk, then I took the girl outside the class and asked her what had happened.

K was trying to peddle goof balls to the students, she explained, and he had become angry when she threatened to tell me what he was doing; and after an exchange of words, he had slapped her. I sent the girl to the washroom to wash her face. Then I took K outside. His eyes were wild and bleary. He began denying everything, saying the girl was a liar and a trouble-maker. Then, suddenly, he became humble, almost meek. I searched him but did not find any drugs on him. Afterwards, I took him to the principal's office.

He was expelled for three days and was not allowed to return until one of his parents accompanied him, to sign for his readmission. (This was his second expulsion.) Later, three weeks before the summer vacation, he was expelled for good—as a result of a third offense reported by another teacher. K started roaming the streets with members of a gang. Sometimes, during the recess period, he would pass by the school and peek through the fence, laughing and talking with the students. Anytime he saw me, he would quickly walk away.

Even though the school's social worker tried to help him,

nothing was settled because school ended and the summer vacation started. One boy recently told me that K is now using hard drugs.

The students will, no doubt, enjoy their summer vacation and will return in the Fall with renewed exuberance, their eyes wide with anticipation of an excellent school year, their youthful minds growing more inquisitive and curious. Of course, their experiences in the surging streets will remain with them and will probably claim some of their lives. The streets teach them many lessons: how to be heartless, brutal, cold; how to despise kindness and laugh at morals; how to cheat, lie, steal; how to kill, maim and destroy. In the Fall there will be many new faces in the classrooms—innocent, hopeful, naive, intelligent faces; faces that know-it-all; faces that yearn for a way out; but, more important, these will be human faces.

A child is shaped and molded by his family. However, in the past thirty or forty years, the role of the family in American culture has changed immensely, in terms of its socializing function. The family can no longer provide the socializing setting it once provided for its members. Other social agencies and institutions have taken over the function of the family.

Unlike the legendary American farm family, which once fulfilled economic, recreational, and religious functions, the modern family, especially in the urban setting, seems to be limited to answering needs for companionship and emotional fulfillment but it does not seem to be doing this very successfully—if the so-called *generation gap* can be used as an index of measurement.

Any teacher, who tries to be a good teacher, should be concerned with the dwindling role of the family and the intellectual and moral development of his pupils. The teacher, in an urban setting especially, is in a strategic position to guide his pupils and instill feelings of self-confidence in them. The classroom teacher is also able to intelligently guide youngsters into activities that mold healthy, well-adjusted personalities. The teacher should attempt to inspire rational thought and individual responsibility in each student, but the drugged mind induces chaotic, illogical thinking—the antithesis of formal education. The teacher should also seek a relationship with the pupils' parents and candidly discuss the social and scholastic performances of the children. Generally speaking, parents are concerned about their children's progress in school. The parents' attitudes toward the child's progress can greatly influence the child's interest in school. Parents can give invaluable information about the child's personality and his strengths and weaknesses. By carefully compiling what a parent relates about the child and his home environment, the teacher can learn if the child feels understood and wanted and loved at home.

Trouble arises when the child thinks that no one cares about him. He thus picks up whatever gimmick society provides—regardless of its moral implications. Since he may think that drugs will rid him of a feeling of loneliness and provide him with a sense of happiness, the youth is liable to become attracted to drugs—first, in sheer experimentation, then for kicks, and later, for whatever pleasures which he can rely upon. Feeling alone, he finds that he needs something upon which to rely, thinking that he can no longer rely upon his parents or the adults in his environment; so finally, he comes to the conclusion that life is nothing more than a seeking of pleasures of the moment.

Immaturity is a major trait of the school-age child. The youth on drugs can be shown the hazards and dangers of drugs, but actually, it must be the youth himself who must learn to face the realities of life.

The thrills a youth seeks when he "goes on" a drug are a search for identity and a desire to be a vital, contributing person. There are many instances of a child's becoming disillusioned as a result of his parents' not viewing him as a unique personality with a destiny of his own.

The teacher can easily show the vast opportunities for today's youth, emphasizing how an individual must seek inner control and maturity in order to plan and attain a happy future. The teacher is instrumental in teaching the child how important a role *self-concept* plays in everyone's life.

The youth on drugs might need psychological evaluation and aid because he is often confronted with various emotional and adjustment problems which he, alone, cannot solve. Such a person may need help in ascertaining his status as a unique individual or he may develop personality problems and suffer from an inability to adjust socially in society.

Often the failure of a youth addicted to drugs to develop logical thinking is a direct result of his not having a proper perspective on life's needs. The young drug addict needs a proper perspective on his role as a contributing member of society. This perspective is indispensable, if he is to learn to cope with the realities of life. A proper perspective aids him in constructing a healthy identity and a healthy sense of his worth as an individual.

Drug abuse should be regarded as a psychological, social, educational, and medical problem which demands that specialists in one field collaborate with specialists in another field, in order to make valuable contributions to an understanding of the problem.

Today's drug problem in the schools is both perplexing and challenging. There is an immense need for understanding the factors which lead many school youths to a reliance on drugs; there is, also, a need for understanding more about the art of counseling the youths in trouble. A youth's dependence on drugs, as a crutch to face reality, constitutes a breakdown in his social role. Any person who has become addicted to drugs has lost his value as a potential contributing member of society. A reliance of drugs instills and reinforces a defeatist attitude in a person. The psychological isolation of such individuals should motivate more research on drug abuse.

Specialists in the psychological and counseling professions are today demanding more comprehensive rehabilitative programs for the drug addict, but teachers must realize that there should, also, be an emphasis on the social adjustment of the individual, realizing at the same time that each student should be taught according to his individual needs.

Chapter VII

PARENTS LOOK AT DRUG ABUSE*

Anonymous*

I know now that my child is a dope addict. It took a long time for my wife and me to discover this fact but now we know, and we are not sure we can do anything about it. After long talks with my son, I discovered that he got his first bag of heroin from a friend and did not beg a pusher on the street for this drug. He tells me that he began sniffing glue at the age of thirteen and then experienced marijuana at parties involving thirteen and fourteen-year-olds. At the age of fifteen he switched to Methedrine (speed) and snorted the powder through his nose. He "dropped acid" (LSD) at the age of seventeen and had his first experience with heroin at the age of eighteen.

My wife and I feel that we are lucky because our son is now at a residential therapy center where he is undergoing treatment for drug addiction. My wife found his "works"—the needle and eyedropper with a plastic pacifier top in his drawer when he was twenty years old. He had been "skin popping" heroin for three years. He had shown many signs of drug addiction during the six or seven years he had been experimenting and while getting hooked on drugs, but evidently his mother and I overlooked most of the signs. Oh, we knew something was wrong from time to time; we thought it was a physical ailment and took him to our family physician. Our son, though, was so skilled and possessed such a great deal of knowledge concerning drugs that the family physician did not discover that he was on heroin. For example, most of his skin popping he did on his legs and feet; therefore, he had no marks on his arms where the physician looked. He did very little "maining" but when he did, he shot under the tongue or between the

---

*This is a true story. The author has requested that he remain anonymous in order to protect his family.

toes which again left very few marks.

He was drowsy a great deal of the time when he was on heroin, and naturally, this should have been a tip-off. But we did not think our son was a dope addict and had no reason to suspect that he was using drugs. Therefore, this was one of the last places that we looked, and, having very little knowledge about drugs ourselves, we were not aware that this condition is as prevalent as it is today. We have since discovered that the prevalence of drug abuse runs very high throughout the United States.

We feel that our son has a chance now because he is in this half-way house with other dope addicts and undergoing group therapy. We intend to give him all the encouragement and assistance that he needs to kick this vicious habit. We have been told that our chances are not good, but we are certainly willing to try because we do not know what else to do.

Our son had abrupt changes of moods when he was fourteen years of age. He lost interest in school, never did develop much interest in dating girls, and did not participate in sports. We know now that probably this was because he was on drugs. He read a lot about drugs and talked a lot about drugs, but we just thought he was interested in keeping up with current events. He was often constipated and did not care too much about eating. We know now that these are signs of drug addiction, but at the time we had no knowledge of drug addiction. Later he began to sleep a lot, acted drowsy, and showed a lack of concern for pain. Again these signs were staring us in the face and we did not realize we were missing the vital signs pointing to drug abuse. At one point, my wife noticed that our son's insteps were bleeding and seemed to be blue and black. He stated that while going barefooted he had stepped on sharp rocks. At a later date he told us that he had injected drugs in the insteps of his feet.

At one point we confronted our son about his nervousness, excessive yawning, and sweating but were told that he was just worried about his school work and would snap out of it in a few days. Naturally he did not snap out of it in a few days.

Chapter VIII

POLICEMEN LOOK AT DRUG ABUSE

PATRICIA BELL*

The following information was obtained through personal interviews conducted at the police department of a city with a population of 75,000 and the local state police headquarters. The interviews were freely given and direct questioning was utilized only upon request by the policemen as to what information the writer felt was pertinent. There were four interviews conducted utilizing three levels of policemen: two detectives, a state policeman, and a sergeant on the educational team on drug abuse for the local high schools.

Questions used to promote responses were as follows: a) What drugs are most used in our area? b) Where are people obtaining drugs in our city? c) What social groups and age groups seem most involved in drug usage? d) How are arrests made of drug users and/or sellers? e) Are the penalties for drug users and sellers heavy enough? f) Will legalization of certain drugs, like marijuana, tend to decrease or increase its use? and g) Do you think school education is helping to curb drug usage?

INTERVIEW 1

According to Detective R, "In a town like this of approximately 75,000 population, the most widely used drugs are the pills such as tranquilizers, sleeping pills, diet pills, etc. A person who uses any type of drug is mentally unbalanced and therefore users should not be severely punished. It is the pushers or sellers of drugs who should be convicted." When questioned on how arrests are made concerning drugs abusers, it was reported, "We use undercover agents who are sent to buy a drug, usually marijuana, from a person under suspicion for selling drugs illegally. Other sources of information come from

---

*Jenkins Memorial Children's Center, Pine Bluff, Arkansas.

reliable informers who have volunteered to act as informants. Some of these informants were at one time users and others were approached to be an informer."

When the writer questioned Detective R as to sources of drugs in our city, he commented, "Sources or availability of drugs are at a low ebb now due to recent investigations which seemed to scare away sellers. But it is a known fact that drugs are being brought into the state from such places as New York State, California, Tennessee (Memphis), Kansas, (Witchita), and Texas. A recent investigation uncovered considerable amounts of marijuana being brought into the city by minority groups and sold at certain business establishments to teen-agers. Further investigations revealed that marijuana was being sent through the mail. This source was squelched by postal inspectors and the involvement of the local postmaster. Due to these uncoverings, drug usage and selling is now few and far between, as no new reports have come through recently. Another investigation of possible availability of drugs was recently uncovered and published in the local newspaper. A deputy sheriff discovered that about an acre of marijuana was found growing just west of the city. Thorough inspection of the area revealed the marijuana was growing wild, but that sections of it had been planted. The field was destroyed by the local authorities."

The writer questioned Detective R about the social groups and age groups most involved in the use of drugs. He stated, "Past investigations and arrests have supported the fact that most users of drugs are between sixteen and twenty-four years of age. Many of these are college students, and this is a part of the problem of control because of these students being transient. Causes for drug usage seem to be not only people with mental problems, but for these kids it is 'the in-thing' to do. It is only a fad and in all probability will pass as do many fads."

"Arrests of pushers are difficult due to lack of information leading to their arrest. After information has been provided, a warrant must be issued for arrest and a search warrant is needed to establish being 'in possession' of drugs. A policeman is concerned with more than the 'oath to enforce the law' concerning drug users. There is a personal concern for the users' health as it has been proven through research that drugs do destroy or cause malfunctions in the cells of the body. Also, if possible, the policeman may help these young people through counseling and possible rehabilitation."

When the writer questioned Detective R about the penalties for drug users and sellers, he remarked, "The laws concerning drug abuse are not severe enough and legalization would not decrease drug usage, because using a drug like marijuana often does lead to the use of 'harder stuff' like heroin. The drug seller is more dangerous than the user and for this reason, penalties should be heavier on him. For the users, convictions depend on why he is taking drugs and if other crimes have been committed by him while under the influence of drugs." Detective R stated the only way to alleviate drug usage and arrests is through "education beginning in the first grade and continuing through all grades. Programs on the Big Brother Club policy could be valuable. Lectures, films, and actual demonstrations of drugs are now used in high schools as the program for education on drugs and its effects."

INTERVIEW 2

Detective P stated, "Kicks are the reasons most kids try drugs. Perhaps booze did not provide the wanted effects, so drugs like marijuana were tried. In older people, perhaps personal problems were too much to bear. The use of drugs in excess could break up marriages and homes and of course, cause harm to reasoning abilities which could lead to accidents causing physical harm to self and/or others."

Detective P further stated, "If a person was sure he would not become hooked on a drug, I personally feel there is no harm in trying something like marijuana. It would provide a kick for a while and wear off. It does not hamper brain functioning and is much like the effect of alcohol on the body which also wears off. But if a person does get hooked, it usually leads to the use of heavier stuff. It does not take many doses of this harder stuff to see a complete change in a person addicted to a drug."

The writer questioned Detective P on the social groups and age groups involved in drug usage. He stated, "Drug abuse does not particularly refer to 'hippies.' It is usually college students, black and white, who use drugs like marijuana or pep pills. There is a lot going on, but it cannot be pinpointed because the general population is unconsciously condoning it by not reporting suspicious people who may well be on drugs. Drug users come from all walks of life, races, and creeds. It seems most prominent among twenty to twenty-four-year-olds, but cases of arrests in this area have been from fifteen to forty-year-olds. Arrests leading to convictions constitute about 99 percent of all cases. Arrests are made through undercover agents, because a person must be 'in possession' for an arrest to be made or very, very reliable witnesses must testify to a person being a pusher." Detective P continued by stating, "Penalties are not heavy enough, especially for pushers. Pushers' punishment should fall somewhere between murder one and two and armed robbery. Since I am a firm believer in capital punishment, I believe a pusher should die or receive life imprisonment the same as on a charge of murder. Convictions depend on many things. The courts are too lenient on both users and sellers. Kids who use drugs for kicks only should be treated differently from those who use drugs or rely on them to commit other crimes."

When asked his opinion about education on drug abuse, Detective P commented to the writer, "No matter what people see on television or read about drugs, individuals will do what they want to do. Education in the schools will help some by instilling a fear into youngsters who are not yet old enough to be approached by a pusher."

INTERVIEW 3

Mr. H, a state policeman, stated, "I am not as involved in drug arrests as are the local police, but I was required to attend a workshop on drugs and all the information I can give you will be either what I was taught or my own opinion."

Mr. H began his comments by stating, "Teen-agers are the highest number of marijuana users. The use of this may and often does lead to the use of harder stuff like heroin. Locally, it is not on a big scale, but is on the increase. College peddlers are now under investigation for transporting drugs in from St. Louis. Of recent arrests made, it is mainly high school dropouts who are most active. Their ages range from eighteen to twenty-two years." Mr. H continued his statements by saying, "It seems alcohol can lead to the use of drugs in order to receive a greater kick quicker. These kicks are often received in a group and seemingly is not a passing thing, like some fads. Often a drug is passed to another person without the person being aware of it."

The writer asked Mr. H how arrests are made of suspicious subjects who might be on drugs and he stated, "If a state policeman is involved in a suspicion arrest, the Criminal Investigation Division is called in on the case and the policemen themselves only help trace, if possible, the source of the drug."

Mr. H made the following comments on legalization. "I feel legalization of drugs would only tend to increase the use of drugs. Some drugs should be taken off the market and tighter controls put on doctors prescribing medicine which might become habit forming. The upper class people seem more involved in the use of these prescription drugs. Average people do not have the problems the rich have and the lower class are not educated enough to worry about their problems."

Mr. H continued his comments by adding, "Detection is a big problem for law enforceers. If a suspect is picked up, it is difficult to get a doctor to perform a blood test. Hospitals will sometimes cooperate, but even if a blood test is run on a person suspected of being under the influence of drugs, the police cannot get a result from the hospital as readily as needed, so samples are sent to the police lab."

The writer questioned Mr. H about education on drug abuse and he made these comments. "Drug abuse is everyone's problem. Anyone connected with or concerned about the coming generation should be involved in its control and education, beginning in the elementary grades will help."

INTERVIEW 4

Sergeant L, a member of the educational team on drug abuse, made the following opening comments. "There are two phases for curbing drug abuse: education and enforcement. Incident reports in our town of 75,000 showed that over the last eighteen months, eighteen cases were arrested. Nine of these were using marijuana and the others were on some type of amphetamines. There is an expected increase in drug usage."

Sergeant L answered the question on education by stating, "It will help to control the use of drugs, but police cannot fight narcotics like other crimes because drug users are sick people and these people must deal with themselves and their problems. The younger children can be reached better. We on the educational team use the 'psychological approach.' We simply show these kids what a drug will do or can do to the body and/or mind and let them draw their own conclusions.

Sergeant L continued by stating, "Most of the people involved in drug usage are between the ages of eighteen and twenty-six. There is some indication of drug usage on our college campus, but it is not near the national statistics for college campuses. These young people are obtaining their drugs through legal prescriptions. They are refilling these prescriptions illegally by going from one drugstore to another so that they can gather larger amounts of the particular drug." He continued by saying, "People using any drug are basically immature. They use drugs as an escape from reality. Teen-agers who use drugs are 'thrill seekers' and try drugs to see the effect for themselves. These teen-agers are usually intelligent and only try drugs because 'everyone else is doing it.'"

The writer questioned Sergeant L about the laws and penalties concerning drug abusers. He stated, "Laws on possession are too strong. A first offense should be classed as a misdemeanor and most of these are now let off on a suspended sentence. A second offense should be classified as a felony and charges should be from one to three years. Possession-for-sale laws are not strong enough. This person is a 'parasite living off human misery' and should receive a minimum of five years and a maximum of fifteen."

Sergeant L continued by saying, "I have found through interviews with addicts that 90 percent of them started on 'grass' (marijuana) and moved on to the 'horse' (heroin). Grass is not habit-forming physically. Psychologically a person may feel he is building up a tolerance on smaller dosages and resort to more and more to benefit from the kick. These addicts are from no particular social or economic status, and your hardened criminal is not in this classification. Hardened criminals will not use drugs to an excess because they too are professionals and drugs make them careless or lax while performing a crime."

Sergeant L summarized his statements by stating, "Drug usage is not a new thing. It dates back as far as time itself. But in our day and time, with its use being illegal and on an increase, there is a need for specially trained police officers and the necessary equipment needed to work better with drug abusers."

Chapter IX

NURSES LOOK AT DRUG ABUSE

CARMEN STOVER*

"People are playing Russian roulette with their lives when they take drugs on their own and not under a doctor's supervision," stated a nurse in discussion drug abuse. "The mind and the body are precision instruments and only a doctor has the knowledge and skill to deal with their mechanisms." Thus she expressed the thinking of four nurses of varying backgrounds.

Interviewed were three registered nurses and a licensed practical nurse. Two work in different hospitals, public and private, and two are school nurses for elementary and junior high schools.

They expressed alarm at the casual way drugs fill the medicine cabinets in our homes. There are pain relievers from aspirin on up, cold tablets, laxatives, tranquilizers, sleeping pills, diet pills, and leftover prescriptions. There are pills for everything. The pattern seems to be one of taking something for relief or pick up at the first symptom or feeling of need. One nurse said, "All their lives children see mama take pills and give them pills. So, what is so new or startling about taking pills on their own or with the group?"

In discussing emergency room experiences, two nurses were angered by the number of children brought in due to drug overdose. Since the children usually are seen soon after the accident, they are given syrup of ipecac and warm water, and situated by a large tub. "It is rough on the kids. How can the parents be so careless!"

Some potentially dangerous drugs of legitimate use are prescribed by doctors. These include the amphetamines and barbiturates. The amphetamines, like Benzedrine and Dexedrine, are stimulants. When properly prescribed they affect the central nervous system by speeding up the body processes, such as

*Child Study Center, University of Arkansas Medical Center, Little Rock, Arkansas.

72

increasing the heart rate and raising the blood pressure. This produces feelings of alertness, self-confidence, and well-being. They act as depressants on the appetite, so are a part of many diet pills. However, the nurses cautioned, that in too heavy dosage, amphetamines cause people to become tense, irritable, jittery, withdrawn, and have slurred speech. They may even seem unable to think clearly. They experience palpitations of the heart, rapid breathing, dilated pupils, dry mouth, sweating, headache, and diarrhea. One nurse warned that if the person was depressed at the time he took a heavy dose of amphetamines it could throw him into a very deep depression that might result in a suicide.

They said the amphetamines were abused by a wide variety of people from housewives to medical students, and businessmen to truck drivers. One nurse said she understood that some sporting asociations have banned their use by athletes.

While these medications are not physically addictive, they recognized that sometimes the body can build up a tolerance to them and larger doses are required to get the desired results. However, they pointed out there was the danger of psychological addiction or dependence on "getting a lift."

As far as they knew, doctors limit the number of refills on prescriptions of amphetamines. However, the barbiturates are more tightly controlled. Here the pharmacist must call the doctor for permission to refill the order. Despite these controls the black market seems to have access to these drugs.

The barbiturates, as Nembutal and Seconal, are sedatives designed to relax the central nervous system. Properly taken, they slow the heart rate, breathing, and lower the blood pressure. They also affect the ability to think, concentrate, and work. Emotional control is weakened and the person becomes irritable and angrily aggressive. He can fall into a deep sleep or coma, which requires medical attention.

Several nurses pointed out some further serious hazards involving barbiturates. Taken with alcohol, they heighten the effect of the alcohol. It has been established that this has been the cause of many automobile accidents. Another hazard is the person becoming confused and taking an overdose resulting in an accidental death. Also, many suicides have been attributed to deep depressions associated with abuse of barbiturates.

The barbiturates are physically addictive; the body requires higher and higher doses to get the desired effect. One nurse said it was her understanding that barbiturate addiction was harder to cure than narcotic addiction. Withdrawal requires a hospital stay of weeks and it takes months for the body to return to normal function.

Their knowledge of federal control of the amphetamines and barbiturates by the Bureau of Narcotics and Dangerous Drugs was limited to the refilling of prescriptions and the strict practices in the hospitals for the accounting of every drug. One nurse explained that not only are the drugs under double lock but that electronic signals are also involved. Another nurse said that with every change of shift the registered nurses going off and coming on duty counted out the medications on hand for an exact reckoning. The various narcotics and their synthetic substitutes, as Morphine, Codeine, and Demerol, are included in this careful hospital procedure.

Addictions can develop during a hospitalization. Though rare, a patient can become physically dependent on a narcotic. The more apt to occur is the psychological addiction, particularly where a patient knows the pain reliever is a synthetic and hence no threat to the body. One nurse said that with all her training and knowledge she experienced such a psychological addiction to a synthetic drug after major surgery. Another nurse said she had a similar experience but that nature had given her a warning by her system totally rejecting all intake. She stopped calling for pain relievers and seemed to improve right away. She did not try to analyze this, but just reported it.

Withdrawal from narcotics is an agonizing experience for the patient. He is restless and nervous, has red eyes and a running nose, diarrhea and cramps, twitching of the extremeties, and pops out in sweat. It is particularly heartrending for the pediatrics nurse to see the newborn infant, addicted as a result of his mother's habit, suffer the withdrawal pains.

One nurse said it might be interesting to know that undiagnosed diabetics show the same symptoms as the heroin addict. These are increased thirst, loss of appetite, and real moodiness. A check of the arms will tell the difference in a hurry ... She also pointed out the dangers involved in using a syringe. The addict takes a terrible chance of infection from nonsterile needles. He can even get hepatitis from a dirty needle.

Another nurse told of the young teen-age drug users brought to pediatrics. She said they were very wary, watching every move the nurse and others make. They require close supervision and much understanding. Of course, they always have problems other than drugs, too. It seems obvious they need extended help and guidance, but she has no way of knowing whether or not it is received.

Two nurses were interested in the treatment for narcotic addicts involving methadone. The patient is maintained on this drug which is also addictive. The difference is that while it keeps the body from craving heroin, it allows the addict a productive life. Methadone maintenance is used on a long-term basis. The nurses said this is not a good program for all patients since it does not work with all.

When an addict has experienced the agonies of withdrawal and his body processes are functioning normally, he must maintain complete abstinence from opiates or he will easily relapse. A high percentage do relapse. One nurse explained, "They go back to the same old neighborhoods, the same old problems, and the same old temptations. They need long-term help and follow-up." She feels the taking of drugs is but a symptom of another problem.

The nurses knew there is a federal law (Narcotic Addict Rehabilitation Act) concerning treatment and rehabilitation of addicts. They did not know its name and were uncertain of its provisions. They did know that there are treatment and research centers in the country. One has a young friend who is an out-patient at such a center. She believed an addict could request treatment in lieu of prosecution under some conditions, but she was very hazy on this point.

LSD frightened all of them because they have no idea of how it works. They understand the functioning of the other drugs with which they deal, but the hallucinogens are "mind-expanders" and do terrible things to a person. One nurse explained a person is never sure of whether he will have a good or bad "trip." Also, the recurring experiences after absence from drug stimulation show many users have little control over such hallucinogenic situations.

What concerned the nurses the most was the possible relationship between chromosome damage and LSD. Leukemia-type syndromes and birth defects have been linked with LSD. They are aware that conclusive studies will take time, but the initial findings are alarming. They are concerned, too, with the ease with which it can be manufactured and its ready availability.

In discussing marijuana, the nurses considered it a light drug when compared to the others. While it is not physically addictive, it most certainly can be *psychologically addictive*. It is a reality-distorting agent and as such is a threat to the young user who is learning to cope with reality as he matures into adulthood. None of the nurses felt its use definitely led to the taking of harder drugs, but did think that such progression occurred in many cases.

One nurse said she was sorry Margaret Mead has given marijuana such support. She thought this would have an influence on many people.

Two of the nurses felt the federal laws making possession of marijuana a felony were too harsh. The other two took the opposite view stating that the offenders were aware of the law and broke it anyway. They held for strict enforcement.

All felt that the crime rate would be reduced if drugs were legalized because the heroin addict would no longer have to turn to larceny or prostitution to get money to feed the habit. However, they did not consider this a good solution to the problem.

All thought education might be the answer. We have to get the facts about the dangers now and in the future to the young people. One thought we need to "scare them to death."

The school nurses in one system have attended lectures at the police department and studied displays to better equip them to educate young people. A school nurse said they have films, film strips, brochures, posters, and other materials on drugs which are worked into the curriculum by the science teachers in junior and senior high schools. However, she thinks the education must begin in elementary school. She first started getting questions two years ago before there was such a furor over drugs. "Believe it or not, the level showing the highest interest in my schools has been the fourth grade." She said the children's knowledge would surprise you. They were curious about syringes, cc's, glue sniffing, and marijuana smoking. She always tries to give honest, truthful answers. Unfortunately, school nurses go to the classroom only on request. Much of their work is clerical.

She also said some junior high students have come for help with individual problems when they did not want to talk to the counselor. She noted their interest in the posters and brochures on drugs that she keeps available. She said the students read the material and return it to her. One caution they give all students is not to accept candy from anyone unless they can vouch for the person. Another warning given to junior and senior high students is not to take a soft drink at a dance unless they have actually seen it being poured. They are never to put a drink down and pick it up later. There is no way of knowing what might have been dropped into it.

One nurse felt we must learn youth's language in order to reach them. "We have to know their terminology to communicate." Another felt that drug taking was a form of rebellion against authority. She also said she thought reformed drug addicts might be the best ones to talk to youth and help them to avoid drug alley or get out of it.

Several of the nurses were concerned about some parents with whom they have dealt. These parents are reluctant to accept the fact they and their children have a drug problem, and other problems, too. "Many people simply cannot face the truth about themselves and their children." She added, "You know, I wonder if we Americans really recognize we have a drug problem. Until we are truthful with ourselves and realize it is right in our own community, we cannot solve it."

Chapter X

A MINISTER LOOKS AT DRUG ABUSE

FRANCES COOPER*

D rug abuse is becoming more common in all areas of American society. The minister will find in his congregation those who use drugs in an abusive way. Since the role of the minister is one of service, he must not overlook or purposely ignore this problem. The minister may logically become active in preventive actions. His counseling role can be helpful to those already involved in drug abuse. His ministry could be valuable to family members of those involved with drugs.

The following questions were used for a broad foundation to explore the involvement of ministers in the drug abuse problem. a) Is the minister adequately informed about drug abuse? b) Does the minister recognize the scope of the drug abuse problem in his community? c) Is the minister now providing services to those involved with drug abuse? d) Does the minister regard drug abuse as a moral problem?

Four ministers from Little Rock, Arkansas, were interviewed using a guide of twenty-five specific questions devised from the broad areas. One of the ministers served a large downtown church whose members come from every section of the city. The other three ministers were pastors of community churches within the Little Rock area. All four men had earned graduate degrees from theological schools and were well trained in their fields. The following report presents a minister's view of the drug abuse problem as suggested by these four pastors.

DEFINITION OF DRUG ABUSE

A minister would define drug abuse in its broadest sense. It includes the drug addict who lives from one "fix" to the next and the teen-ager who smokes marijuana in an effort to keep

---

*Hardin-Bale, Little Rock, Arkansas.

79

up with the crowd. It would also include the businessman who finds tranquilizers a necessity to his hectic life and the housewife who takes diet pills to give her extra energy. One minister who was interviewed felt that some doctors abuse the use of drugs by prescribing them when it is not necessary to the treatment of the patient. The abusive use of drugs is practiced in dirty alleys of slum sections, in the halls of junior and senior high schools, and at times, in the elementary school. The matter may be a private affair or carried on in a social gathering. It may be an enslaving habit or an occasional occurrence. To the minister, any use of any drugs except those prescribed for current treatment by a competent physician would constitute drug abuse.

PREVALENCE OF DRUG ABUSE

The minister recognizes that the abuse of drugs is increasing and believes it to be more acute among the teen-age population. Many reasons were suggested for this rise in the prevalence of drug abuse. The easy access most young people have to drugs today was cited often. The lack of parental awareness of the extent of the problem has contributed to this rise. The general unconcern of parents about the activities of their children allows young people to become involved with drugs more often. The example that the adult population sets was also mentioned. Many adults find it necessary to use some type of stimulant, usually alcohol, to relax or to have a good time. The youth simply imitates the action of his parents or other adults but chooses to use a stimulant other than alcohol. Perhaps he uses drugs in addition to alcohol. In this way he seeks to have a good time or to "let himself go." The minister believes that much of the responsibility for the increase in the use of drugs among young people must be placed on the adult population.

The rise in problems related to drug abuse does not seem to be limited to any socioeconomic level. Most of the ministers interviewed referred to the fact that the affluent youth of today has money with which to buy drugs. Parents require no accounting for the use of this money and therefore, the youth spends it without reservation. However, the minister also recognizes that a young person in the lower socioeconomic levels has many accesses to drugs. Young people are often unsupervised and can easily become prey of those who want to broaden their market for the sale of drugs. In general, the minister sees a rise of drug abuse at all socioeconomic levels. He suggests that at the upper socioeconomic level there is a great amount of experimenting with drugs while addictive abuse seems to be more prevalent in the lower strata.

These observations are made by the minister from general knowledge and information. Only one of the ministers interviewed reported that he had had any personal contact with a person directly involved in the use of drugs. Ministers hear of the drug traffic and practices among young people from their association with the youth of their churches. Only occasionally does the adult congregation discuss this problem with the minister. Those interviewed all prefaced their remarks with similar statements indicating that they had very little direct personal knowledge of this problem. They felt that those involved with the problem deliberately concealed it from the minister. Therefore, most ministers are not aware of the extent of the problem in their communities. The four men who were interviewed said that they did not believe that there is a current drug abuse problem in their particular area. However, they agreed that it is a festering sore in their city and poses a threat to every community. They anticipate more personal encounter with the problem.

CAUSES OF DRUG ABUSE

Why would a young person become involved in the abusive use of drugs? The minister, as well as the educator and the policeman, would search for the answers to this question. The ministers interviewed made the following observations in their response to this query.

There is much emphasis in American life today on humanistic freedom. To do your own thing is a goal held high in esteem. This emphasis has allowed the young person to grow up with more freedom than has been known in the past. Many of these youths are not able to handle the responsibilities of this freedom. Their response may be an extreme reaction and sometimes includes the use of drugs.

Boredom with the scope of his life may at times cause a young person to experiment with drugs. The affluent youth finds the easy life begins to drag. The youth in a low socio-economic level is bored by the limitations of his existence. Both groups seek to escape.

Some young people are disillusioned with the quality of American life as a whole. They reject the values and systems that are a part of our society. They resent the hypocrisy which they feel exists among adults. Rejection and resentment are shown in many ways with drug abuse being one of them.

Acceptance by the general public was cited as another reason why a young person would become involved with drugs. Smoking marijuana is considered acceptable in many circles today. Stimulating drugs are often regarded as desirable. Young people read about and hear the idols of the entertainment field give approval to the use of some drugs. The general tone of society as it speaks about drugs subtly influences the thinking of today's youth.

Society must also bear the blame for a general lowering of moral standards which contributes to the drug abuse problem. Many groups would believe that there are no absolutes of morality. The minister sees the lack of a strong moral code in our society as a contributing factor to the abusive use of drugs.

Young people have a natural tendency to rebel against authority and to experiment as a part of the maturing process. The pressure of peer groups is keenly felt at this age. These factors are sometimes the controlling influence during this time. The fact that drugs are readily available would encourage the use of them during this period of life. Few young people have an adequate understanding of the consequences of these actions.

The minister today sees a complexity of factors which contribute to the involvement of a young person with drugs. Basically, he sees it as the fault of modern society. He sees the young person as responsible for his actions but also as a product of the influences upon him.

MORAL ISSUES

Ministers feel that drug abuse is morally wrong. They cite the damaging effect drugs have on the body and the mind. They believe that the body and the mind are a trust from God and should not be abused. The ability of the mind to reason is the factor that distinguishes man from other animals. To impair this reasoning ability is wrong.

Furthermore, the damaging effect on other members of society when drugs are used is a moral issue. Damage to other men is an accompanying characteristic of the abuse of drugs. The minister would believe that for this reason the abusive use of drugs is an immoral act.

THE MINISTER'S RESPONSIBILITY

Primarily, the minister views his responsibility in the preventive area. Programs of information for young people and adults were cited. Two of the ministers interviewed spoke of several programs in their churches to provide information and caution to the congregation. These programs involved information given by medical men, police personnel, and a group of young men who had been addicted to drugs. They also used films and discussion groups.

The minister also sees as his responsibility the teaching of a strong and absolute moral code for youth and adults alike. He believes that the emphasis should go beyond being a part of the church to a vital relationship with God.

Counseling is also seen as a part of the minister's responsibility when he does have direct contact with persons involved with drugs. However, all the ministers interviewed acknowledged their lack of training in this field and felt that apart from spiritual counseling, they should act only as a referral source. Supportive counseling might be continued after referrals are made.

The minister's role would include working toward general

public awareness of the problem. In general, the public is unaware of the extent of the problem and usually expresses surprise when drug abuse becomes evident in the local area. The minister's responsibility includes cooperation with community agencies in every effort to make the public aware of the problem.

A revision of current laws to make it a more serious offense to be charged with selling or using drugs would be a point of emphasis. The current laws are not strict enough. The minister feels that heavy penalities would be a strong deterrent to the selling of drugs and to the use of drugs in an abusive way. There is a need for more strict enforcement of the laws by the police. An expansion of the police force to provide this service was suggested. The minister would consider it a civic responsibility to work for improvement in these areas.

CONCLUSIONS

The minister has only general knowledge about the drug abuse problem. He has acquired this information from a source other than his training or personal experience. He is not aware of the scope of drug abuse in his community though he senses the threatening nature of the problem. The minister considers drug abuse a moral problem and believes one important way to curb it is through the general acceptance of a strong moral code. He believes he has a positive role to play in meeting this problem.

Chapter XI

SCHOOL ADMINISTRATORS LOOK AT DRUG ABUSE

Mary Alice Acklin*

R eports from all over the nation indicate that the use and abuse of drugs is prevalent in virtually every segment of society today. Indications are that the condition is widespread and its severity increasing. It has become a matter of concern to persons in various positions and professions. Emphasis has been placed on student groups as users, abusers, and pushers. Is this really a valid accusation? How do school administrators view the various aspects of the problem?

Personal interviews were arranged with school administrators from many levels and in communities of unequal populations. Men and women who serve as principals and/or supervisors of elementary and secondary schools answered questions pertaining to the following: a) a definition of use and abuse of drugs, b) differences between hard and soft drugs, c) problems in the community and individual schools, d) means of detection, e) methods of handling, f) laws and law enforcement, and g) possible solutions. Each administrator expressed his views openly and with obvious awareness of the pressing need for an effective solution.

Most of the administrators questioned in the interviews defined drugs as those medicines which are habit forming. Some referred to drugs as mind expanders, stimulants, and depressants. Only two of the group saw drugs as "everything from an aspirin up." One went so far as to call "any medicine" a drug. In reference to hard and soft drugs, all but one of those interviewed felt a difference existed. The exception was one high school principal who saw "little difference in what it is—a drug is a drug whether it is aspirin or heroin."

---

*Holman Elementary, Stuttgart, Arkansas.

The greatest percentage thought both use and abuse of drugs to be increasing. All those taking part in the interviews described abuse as the use of any medication, whether prescribed by a physician or not, beyond the intent of the doctor. One principal felt that reliance on any drug constituted abuse and another expressed the feeling that all people rely on drugs.

Recognition of drug abuse as a community problem was advanced by administrators in larger cities and college towns. In the smaller communities it was felt that there were a few cases of abuse but the urgency was to prevent the infiltration of drug suppliers and pushers to the extent that it would remain a relatively minor problem for the community. None of those questioned would venture a percentage figure but all felt that great numbers "experimented" with the hard drugs, and even more continued to use prescribed medication long after the intent of the physician. They advanced the belief that more adults than youths created community problems.

Enumerated as effects on the community were such items as the increase of petty crimes, degeneration of positive attitudes toward law and law enforcement personnel, lowered moral and ethical standards, and increased tension between divergent groups.

In schools of the larger communities and college towns a greater percentage of the student body was thought not only to use drugs, but also to use a greater variety of types. Some things that were not classified as drugs (e.g., peanut butter) were reported used in one large school. Secondary principals in smaller towns felt that a large percentage of the high school population tried drugs on occasion, usually at social functions, but few were addicted. It was thought that young people in one community remained in close social contact with college students who became the spreaders of the drugs following their own experimentation on campus. Easy access to the medicine cabinet in the home was cited as another factor in student trial of drugs.

The detection of student users posed a difficulty for administrators since manifestations were not easily isolated from behavior

which stemmed from other causes. The thought that most drugs
were tried in groups gathered at evening youth activities account-
ed for the fact that suspects were almost impossible to detect.
Most visible effects were gone or diminished by the following
day. Information concerning students who were suspect usually
came from other students who reported them or from doctors
who sought the aid of school personnel. In only one case had
any administrator been able to corroborate his or her suspicions.
Those at elementary level had no knowledge of any individuals
that needed observation; hence, they had employed no means
of detection.

Questions about their methods of handling the individual
who was indulging in drugs yielded a variety of responses.
Those who had never been faced with this decision began with
"I don't know" and projected possibilities. The usual method
seemed to be a personal conference with the offender, followed
by consultation with the school counselor and parents of the
student. The final move was to report findings to legal authorities.
Administrators who had been called upon to meet with suspect
students felt they had had little, if any, success.

Lowered respect for authority was seen to be the paramount
effect on the school population. Principals advanced the theory
that their limited exposure to a severe or complex involvement
in the drug abuse problem prevented them from making first-
hand observations. Consequently their opinions were, in effect,
suppositions of how they felt.

The dominant opinion of most administrators in regard to
existing laws was seen to be a need for more adequate definition
of offenses and realistic revisions of present policies. The purpose
of revision was fourfold: a) to protect the general society, b)
to effect treatment for users, c) to provide mandatory treatment
for pushers, and d) to severely prosecute suppliers. One administrator voiced the opinion that laws were too severe for users,
whom he saw as patients, and too lenient for providers of
drugs, whom he saw as criminals. Users were defined as experi-
menters and new addicts, pushers as addicts and spreaders of
drugs, and suppliers as nonusers who provided drugs as a

business enterprise. All would impose heavy penalties upon those who supply drugs to others.

The greatest variation of responses was in regard to law enforcement. The range of opinion was expressed as, a) no enforcement, b) no follow-up reported cases, c) inadequacy of trained law enforcement personnel, d) a lack of concern or blind disregard in some agencies, e) sufficient in his own community, and f) extremely well organized. In one instance a secondary principal had observed a student at the request of a physician, determined his source of supply, and reported it to local authorities. Local authorities had pursued the investigation, called upon federal agencies to investigate further and lend assistance in apprehending the violator. Federal authorities conferred with the administrator and expressed regret that they could not be of immediate service because of a shortage of personnel and the numerous cases already pending. The administrator felt that such delays rendered the investigation and subsequent evidence as virtually useless.

The approach to possible solutions was generally thought to be in the nature of education, but there was diverse opinion as to what type of program(s) to employ and where to initiate said program(s). Suggested programs were the following: a) use of individual and group counseling in school and church groups, b) films in classrooms, c) all-school programs with individual speakers and panels, and d) advice from parents. In working with student groups, one principal suggested use of workshop training for existing student leaders followed by small classroom groups in workshops led by these trained students. He reasoned that most students respond more frequently to the peer group. The same principal attributed much of the total problem to lack of communication and ignorance of methods of interpersonal relationships, especially between adults and youth. At least one administrator, formerly of a large community, regarded drug abuse as a cyclical problem beginning with a fad, followed by education which enlightened the population to the dangers and effects of drugs, and finally the cessation of use except in a very low percentage of individuals who were "hooked." Yet another felt that there was no program that would exterminate the problem but that education could lessen it. A great hindrance to any program was thought to be lack of necessary funds and experts to train personnel in techniques of combating the existing problem and preventing its further spread.

In evaluating conclusions drawn from these interviews several limitations were recognized. The relatively small number of persons contacted could only approximate a narrow cross section of opinions. The respondents were all of a central geographical location and of one profession. Although those interviewed seemed vitally interested in the questions, there is the possibility of hasty response. Based on current publications, commentaries, and statistics, the greatest proportion of school administrators interviewed seemed adequately aware of the existence of the problem as related to their community and schools. Their opinions were as diverse as those voiced by experts in the field. In areas of widely accepted points of view the administrators were in accord. There was a proliferation of views as to the type and quality of law enforcement. Outcomes of the interviews exposed the need for further research as to the most feasible approach to effective educational techniques. There was implication that insufficient knowledge exists concerning drug abuse by adults. That this condition has caused the young to view use of drugs as acceptable or even desirable has been expressed by some experts. Lack of direct contact with involved persons might account for the lack of this perspective.

Results of the interviews indicated that administrators saw as valid the accusation that use is widespread and is increasing in most locations, but the majority of them stipulated that adults were the principal offenders. The interviewer saw no indication that administrators treated the problem lightly even when they felt that it posed no special problem for them in their particular position. Persons included in the interviews were representative of two races, both sexes, and several academic levels. The total number of participants was seven. They represented communities of three distinct sizes; less than 2,500; approximately 10,000; and greater than 100,000. Regardless of the variables cited, the findings of the several interviews revealed that school administrators were alerted to the prevalence of drugs and drug use in the society and felt responsibility toward the community as well as the school.

Chapter XII

A STUDENT LOOKS AT DRUG ABUSE

SHARON*

The destruction is now complete. The misery, violence, and torment is over for you but not for the rest of us. But I shall always wonder why—why it had to be this way. Why life for you had to be such a nightmare that caught all of us up into it, too.

I have just finished reading a letter you wrote Edward and me fifteen years ago to be given to us at the time of your death. And even in it you seem to be so helpless and to be so afraid to face reality. My father—"the best doctor in the whole world"—was what I used to write in every letter I ever sent you. As a child my friends could not be around me five minutes without finding out my dad was a doctor. I was so proud of you even though I continuously tried to hide from everyone that knew anyway something I did not understand myself.

You were 6 feet 3 inches tall, usually weighed 250 pounds, and looked so powerful. Yet you were so weak you had to find strength in drugs. Only now do I realize how very dependent you were on others and how badly you needed to be reassured continuously of our love.

It is ironical that you and Mom should both achieve destruction at the same time. Though Mom is not quite dead yet, she has recently been placed in a state hospital as the result of continuous drinking and taking drugs. You two could have had the whole world if you had wanted it. What happened to turn you into such lifeless shells? I look on you and mother and our brief life together and I am confused and hurt. I know I shall never understand why my Dad had to suffer so and in turn hurt us so. The scars that your torment left on Edward and me will never quite heal.

---

*This chapter was written by a college student who prefers to remain anonymous. The story is true but the names have been changed.

You once told me you wanted me to have your medical books someday. But every time I look at them and think how hard you studied and read them and what a wonderful doctor you could have been and what a wonderful life we could have had together as a family, then the hurt starts all over again. Doctors that worked with you and teachers that knew you in medical school have many times told me what a brilliant man you were. Though you graduated first in your medical class, this knowledge of medicine, drugs, symptoms, and cures you willingly prescribed to others, but could not seem to use to treat yourself. Your life seems like such a waste, Dad. I think that is what hurts the most. I remember as a child that I would look up some topic in your medical books just to get you to talk to me. Most of the time I had no idea what we were talking about, but you were talking to me and that was all that mattered. It bothers me a great deal to think your only memories will be those of a few of your family, friends and patients.

I remember as children when Edward and I would come visit you in the summers that the first thing we would do would be to find a hiding place so that when Dad got "sick" we could go there.

When you were under the influence of drugs, you could be so surprisingly violent. So many times I have seen you screaming like an animal, breaking furniture, beating up on whichever mother we had at the moment, and I will never forget the sound of my voice screaming at you to stop. I remember the Christmas you kept hitting my third mother over and over and I was hitting you, trying to get you to stop, and Edward was crying because we were making so much noise. Or the time you threw my eighteen-month-old half-brother against the wall or the time you broke the coffee table in two with your hand. And once when I was about ten years old, I remember seeing you shaking so hard you could not get a syringe into your arm and kept asking me to push it in for you. I will never forget the night of my high school graduation when Virginia called and said that you were in jail for trying to kill a man and had lost your medical license. Violence seemed to be so much a part of our lives.

But at the same time you could be so unnaturally gentle. I remember the time I pulled the lamp off on my head and your oversized hands put twelve stitches in my forehead so skillfully that even today there is no scar. One of my most tender memories is the time I came running into your office packed with patients crying because Blackie, my dog, had just been run over, and you sat me on your lap and talked to me for a long time. I will never forget that. It seems like I was always hugging you and wanting you to respond to me. But you never seemed to be quite able to receive or to give love.

I try to remember the fun we had, but those are such few and precious memories. I remember when you used to take Edward and me swimming and how much fun we would have. Or I wonder how many times I have seen you sitting on the front porch singing and playing the "Blues" on your guitar? But then you and Mom would start fighting and it would start all over again.

You told me that it killed you when the court took Edward and me away from you for Papa and Emma to raise. But if we really meant that much to you, why couldn't you stop?

After you were fired at the sanatorium for stealing drugs, Virginia took my half-brother and left you. I think of all the mothers that Edward and I had, that she was the closest you ever came to really loving. After she left, you went to the state hospital for "rest." I'll never forget the day Papa brought you home. You looked like a broken down old man. You were shaking and we had to help you up the stairs and to undress. Then came the period of torment for all of us. When I came in from college on the weekends to see you, you would just sit there and never say a word. If you ever answered me it would be to echo something I had said, or you would continuously talk about the past and my real mother and things you two had done and would ask me to remember in such a way that was both pathetic and frightening. You let your food and cigar ashes fall on the floor and sometimes you would lie down on the rug and sleep for four or five hours without moving. Many nights have I listened to see if you were still breathing and many times have I tiptoed to your door to just make sure you were all right. You were like a vegetable and I will never forget how it hurt me when you would tell me how you wanted to die and how no one loved you when I loved you so much my heart was aching. We all loved you, Dad. I wish I knew how else we could have proved that to you.

I just now looked down at the threadbare cloth of the arms on the chair in which I am sitting. How many times I have seen you sit in this chair rubbing your hands back and forth and grinding your teeth over and over. How many times I have wondered what kind of agony your mind was going through. How much I always wanted to help you. But there was nothing any of us ever seemed to be able to do.

I cannot stand to see the hurt and guilt in Papa and Emma's eyes, I guess it must really be horrible to watch a baby grow into a man and then see him fall. So many times have I seen Papa cry and ask God to help you. At your funeral Papa asked me over and over again if you had ever belonged to a church. Forgive me, because I told him you once belonged to the Methodist Church in Clear Springs, though I know you never did. But it meant so much to him to think you at one time did. And Emma asks me over and over if I thought you knew she loved you. She keeps telling me about how good you were when you were a little boy and how you once told her you had never been happy since you left home.

Oh, Dad, I wish I could talk to you one more time. I wish you could tell me what made you so afraid to face reality, why you had to continuously hide from it—but then I wonder if you ever really knew yourself.

I am glad you did get to see your first grandchild. The few times you seemed to come out of your world and back into ours was when you were holding Susie in your lap. Then you would smile and for a moment be happy.

Papa's pastor told me that it was too late to save you, because you were in hell, and that I had better start doing some serious repenting. I must believe that in death you have finally found the answer to questions you seemed to be hopelessly trying to find. You lived in a hell, Dad, that I am sure God could not equal. I must believe you found peace in a release from a life with which you just could not seem to cope.

INDEX